Praise for Alzheimer's (

"Gift. That was the concept repeating itself in my mind as I read this book: a gift. So, it was a delight to see Jane end with this very word. That is what this book is: a gift from Sky and Jane. A gift of vulnerability and validation. A gift of truth-telling and humility. A gift in two voices: from two people living with dementia, one caregiver sharing with exquisite frankness; one with a brain riddled with plaque, sharing with rare and powerful candor (and sometimes irreverent humor). Like I said: a gift for us all."

—*Rev. Karen G. Johnston,*
founder, Date with Death Club

"This exquisite and intimate book is like a love letter from an unknown address. Jane Dwinell and Sky Yardley take us on a journey with them into the uncharted world of Alzheimer's Disease. They bravely navigate the depths of Alzheimer's Canyon, shining a light in a disorienting landscape. Their unflinching honesty about their lived experience serves as an emotional road map for anyone facing an unexpected challenge. Out of her grief, Dwinell offers this gift, and hope."

—*David Goodman, bestselling author and host,*
The Vermont Conversation

"A remarkable read. Jane and Sky take the reader through the whirlwind that is dementia. From the moment they both knew something had changed to the moment they received a formal diagnosis all the way to end of life. A beautiful life.

While each journey through dementia is unique, the lessons that Jane and Sky learned and share with the reader can be embraced by all: Practice patience. I say practice because it does not come easily for all; give yourself permission to grieve and find support systems to help through this journey, and cherish the moments where love shines through, whether it be a lucid moment, a gentle touch, or a knowing smile.

While I was only privileged to know Sky for a short period of time, he quickly became one of my favorite people. Sky invited me on all kinds of adventures, whether it was building a boat, fixing a broken item in the community, or helping on the farm. What always drew me to Sky was that he was an incredibly empathetic person and could feel the energy of others. Sky would be quick to observe someone feeling down or off and became my emotional observer, which for a social worker was a true gift to have.

I feel truly honored to have known Sky and to have gotten to know Jane and their family."

—*Samantha Wendel CMC, CSA, CDP,*
Director of Resident and Family Services

ALZHEIMER'S CANYON

ENTRY LABEL

THIS FORM MUST BE INCLUDED INSIDE THE FRONT COVER OF
EACH BOOK YOU SUBMIT, therefore cut it from here and duplicate it as often as necessary. Insert the label inside the front cover
of each book submitted (if you enter one book in one category,
you must insert this form into each of the four books sent).

FOR AUDIOBOOKS: please send 3 Audible gift codes to Terry
Nathan at terry@ibpa-online.org. If your book is not available
on Audible, please contact Terry Nathan for additional options.

18. Health + Fitness

CATEGORY (NO. AND NAME)

Alzheimer's Canyon

TITLE

Jane Dwinell

CONTACT PERSON

Rootstock Publishing

PUBLISHER

1106 North Ave.

CONTACT PERSON'S ADDRESS

Burlington VT 05408

CONTACT PERSON'S CITY, STATE, ZIP

802 377 1712

CONTACT PERSON'S TELEPHONE

janedwinell@gmail.com

CONTACT PERSON'S EMAIL

janedwinell.com

WEBSITE ADDRESS

Please indicate the book's target audience:

People w/ dementia, their loved
ones + health care providers

ALZHEIMER'S CANYON

One Couple's Reflections on Living with Dementia

BY JANE DWINELL & SKY YARDLEY

Montpelier, VT

First Printing: 2022
Copyright © 2022 by Jane Dwinell
All Rights Reserved.
Release Date: November 1, 2022

Softcover ISBN: 978-1-57869-111-1
Hardcover ISBN: 978-1-57869-112-8
eBook ISBN: 978-1-57869-113-5

Library of Congress Control Number: 2022905792

Published by Rootstock Publishing
an imprint of Multicultural Media, Inc.
27 Main Street, Suite 6
Montpelier, VT 05602 USA

www.rootstockpublishing.com
info@rootstockpublishing.com

For permissions or to schedule an author interview, contact the author at janedwinell@gmail.com.

"Do Not Go Gentle Into That Good Night," by Dylan Thomas, from THE POEMS OF DYLAN THOMAS, copyright ©1952 by Dylan Thomas. Reprinted by permission of New Directions Publishing Corp.

Cover and interior design by Dana Dwinell-Yardley (ddydesign.com).

Author photo by Valerie Stoller

Printed in the USA

To all those living with dementia—
may you always feel the love
of your family and friends,
even if you don't know who they are.

PROLOGUE

This book tells the story of one couple's journey through the twisted canyons of Alzheimer's disease. It is a compilation of posts we wrote over the course of four years to share our experience on our blog, supplemented with some additional narrative from me (Jane) for context. But of course, Sky's and my story began long before his diagnosis in 2016. We met in the summer of 1984. I had just opened a vegetarian restaurant in central Vermont—the Corner Cafe—and Sky was my Thursday afternoon produce delivery man. He and the other guys who delivered my produce were always upbeat, interested in what I was serving, and happy to educate me about the ins and outs of produce—what was in season, what was a good deal, what I should avoid. Even though I loved cooking and had been an avid gardener for years, I learned a lot from these fellows.

Before too long, I began to look forward to Thursday afternoon in particular, and I began to connect more deeply with Sky after he wore a T-shirt from the town where I had gone to college. Soon, we had more to talk about than produce. I discovered we had a lot in common. Besides, he was cute.

By Valentine's Day 1985, I was brave enough to ask him out: Would he like to come over for cross-country skiing and dinner on his way to the Boston market? By March, we were a couple, and in December, I sold my restaurant and moved in with him in the cabin we had built together.

Life went on from there. In 1986, we bought forty-five acres in northern Vermont where we planned to homestead, build a passive solar house, grow food, live off-grid, make maple syrup, and start a family. Dana joined us in 1987, Sayer in 1990. In and amongst the homesteading chores, Sky went to school to become a mediator, and set up his own practice helping families with divorce and child custody arrangements. I worked part time as an RN at a local nursing home's memory care unit and started my freelance writing career. We homeschooled our kids. Life was good.

Craving more community and more meaning in my life, in 1994 I started divinity school on the other side of the country, while working part time as a hospice nurse. Sky, Dana, and Sayer were good sports, looking at our California years as an adventure: riding bikes, swimming, hiking, traveling, and hanging out with other homeschoolers. Sky learned firsthand what it was like to be a stay-at-home parent, and he was good at it. It was a gift to me, and after two years, my degree in hand, we moved back to our homestead.

Sky and I continued our partnership back in Vermont. I became the minister of a small local Unitarian Universalist church, and Sky, the church administrator. We were both committed to working part time so as to have time for Dana and Sayer, and the homestead.

Time passed. Soon Dana and Sayer were teens, and Sky and I felt the pull to move on, try something new, provide more opportunities for our kids. We moved to a small Vermont city in 2004, and started over. Together, the four of us built another passive solar house. We settled into our new community, me working as a small congregation consultant, Sky starting up a new mediation practice, and the kids making new friends and seeking their own paths into adulthood.

After a few years, Sky and I started getting restless. He was increasingly frustrated with the high-conflict families he was working with, frustrated that he couldn't get the parents to understand that they were hurting their children by continuing to fight and bicker, always putting the kids in the middle, a no-win situation. I was ready for something new, another challenge. We started tossing ideas around, and spent some time trying a few things out. Nothing clicked.

Until—pretty much out of nowhere—we got the idea to buy a houseboat in France and cruise the canals. We scoured the internet for boats and information. We read the few books we could find. Sky and I shared a love of being on the water, having both grown up spending summers on small New England lakes. In our years together, we had managed to acquire a canoe, three kayaks, and two sailboats. On a two-month European tour with Dana and Sayer in 2007, we started looking at boats. And fell in love.

Antinous was a nine-meter, clunky-appearing steel boat that was perfect for us—lots of big windows, small bedroom, head, shower, galley, sitting area, and a petite terrasse. We practically bought her on the spot. Dana and Sayer thought this idea was, well, preposterous. But they could see how happy we were, so they supported us in this new endeavor.

Soon we were off. Once we realized we had no idea what we were doing—how to drive such a boat, how to traverse locks, what canal etiquette entailed—we learned as much as fast as we could. Watching other boaters, talking to people, making many mistakes, taking *Antinous* out to practice when no one was watching—hands-on was the answer. Every day was a challenge, and a gift. France was a beautiful country, and being on the water with magnificent plane trees bordering the canal, quaint villages with ancient architecture, and the peace of aquatic life was amazing. Every evening, we would sit on our terrasse, glasses of wine in hand, marveling at our good luck to have discovered this life.

Back home, we considered next steps. We couldn't wait to get back to France, but what about Dana and Sayer, what about our careers? Since the canals were only open from April until October (and, theoretically, we were not allowed to stay in France for more than ninety days every year), what would we do with ourselves for the rest of the year? Sky couldn't abandon his mediation practice for periods of time like that, though I might be able to continue to consult. Perhaps volunteering? Along with our "professional" skills, we also knew how to build and renovate houses. Hurricane Katrina had ravaged the Gulf Coast in 2005, and the area was still in need of help in the spring of 2008 when we headed south with our tools and camping equipment.

We loved New Orleans, Sky especially. We met some great people, ate fabulous food, and listened to amazing music. We helped with one housebuilding project (on twelve-foot-high stilts in case of another flood) and another house in need of a complete renovation. We listened to Katrina stories from everyone we met. People were still devastated, still traumatized by the loss of so much. On one of our last days there, two of our new friends asked if we would like to buy the empty lot next to their house . . . and move there.

It was more to think about as we floated around the canals of France that summer. New Orleans? But we were Vermonters, country folk. What about Dana and Sayer? What about my elderly mother? By the time we decided to do it, someone else had bought the property. So much for that. But fate intervened, and six months later, we got a call—another property in the neighborhood had opened up—were we still interested?

Yes, we were! In the meantime, I had secured a consulting job in England for the month of April, after which we would head for France and more adventures aboard *Antinous*. It was a different kind of summer for us. We had the usual boating adventures, learned about hand-cranked locks and the scariness of driving in a tunnel. We met other boaters and, at times, shared crazy days and bottles of wine. We started talking about the house we would build in New Orleans—a different climate with different expectations. Lifelong environmentalists, we talked about the impact on the climate of our flights across the Atlantic, and all the diesel we burned having so much fun. We had looked into converting *Antinous*'s engine to biodiesel but discovered that that was illegal in France. Should we convert *Antinous* to all-electric, or should we just sell and stay put in one place? So much to think about.

Before we left for England and France, we had rented our Vermont house and put our belongings into storage. Dana and Sayer had moved into another house in town with a bunch of their friends. Dana and Sayer had jobs and sweethearts, and the roommates all seemed to be getting along well, so when we returned to Vermont from France in the fall of 2009, we packed our tools, clothes, and a few other belongings into a small trailer and headed for New Orleans.

On to the next adventure! We rented an apartment near our friends and our house site. We planted gardens and fruit trees. We continued working on house plans. We ran up against all the post-Katrina housing rules: to build a house now required both architectural plans as well as hurricane-proof engineering plans. We had always designed our houses ourselves, drawing rooms, doors, and windows on big pieces of graph paper. Now we had to find an architect who would listen to our unique ideas and get them on paper for approval by the city. The architect would find the engineer, thank goodness. I became impatient with the wait—I wanted to start building! Sky, being more patient than I, kept me calm. Finally, the paperwork was done, everything approved, and in March 2010, we broke ground.

It was a wild and challenging spring building our two-story "cupola house," nine feet in the air. Neither Sky nor I was fond of heights, but we soldiered on. A new friend who was not acrophobic helped out on occasion. Our goal was to get it framed up and enclosed by June. We loved building houses, working together in partnership, and reveled in watching a house start to take shape, fantasizing about what it would be like to live there. Amidst the house building, we continued to take part in the musical and culinary joys of New Orleans, hanging out with new friends. Life was good as we fled the hot weather for a summer in Vermont and France.

But clouds were gathering on the horizon. My elderly mother had undergone successful surgery for colon cancer, but she began to have trouble with periodic adhesions that would land her in the hospital. She began falling a lot. She lived alone in the five-bedroom house where I and my brothers had grown up, refusing to move to a condo or senior living community, or at the very least, have someone come and live with her. Her hospitalizations became more frequent, and it was clear she could no longer live alone. Despite her being upset by it, my brothers and I placed her in assisted living—assuring her at the time it was only temporary until she regained strength enough to go home—and she agreed to have someone live with her.

All this was going on while Sky and I were back in New Orleans in the fall of 2010 trying to finish the house so we could move in. But things went from bad to worse with my mother, and I had to return to Vermont to watch over her, her house, her finances, and her three rental properties. It was a bad time. Sky stayed in New Orleans to work on the house—we were up to finish work at that point, something Sky generally did without my help, enjoying the slow, careful work of trim, kitchen cabinets, and flooring. We hated being apart, but we did manage a couple of trips back and forth to see one another. Given the situation with my mother, it was clear we would not be going back to France anytime soon, so we looked into the possibility of buying a boat to live on in the U.S.

Things began to fall into place in the spring of 2011. A young couple with three kids had approached me about buying my mother's house, and she agreed to sell (her condition had continued to decline and it was clear she would not be able to go home again). Sky and I found a boat on the coast of Maine, and bought it. The plan was to work on it (it was in serious need of repair) and then sail it to Lake Champlain, where we would moor it for the summer. Sayer joined Sky in New Orleans to do what work they could to secure the house for the summer, and then they headed back to Vermont. Sky and I moved to Maine to live aboard *Patience* once my mother's house was sold.

Then the nightmare began. *Patience* needed way more work than we were expecting, and the people at the marina were less than helpful, resenting that we were doing the work ourselves rather than hiring their crew. We would fix one system, only to discover more problems with another system. We only managed to leave the dock once. After six weeks, we decided to sell her and cut our losses. We began looking at other boats. We moved into a room over a friend's garage. My mother's health continued to decline, and with her increasing frailty and dementia, she became increasingly angry at me, telling me I had tricked her into selling her house, and that I cared for no one but myself. Visiting her was painful. Life was not good.

Not knowing when we might be able to return to either New Orleans or France, Sky and I returned to our home after asking our renters to leave. We had no idea what to do with ourselves. We applied for some jobs, we picked up some volunteer work, and Sky eventually landed a job helping people who had been affected by Tropical Storm Irene, which had devastated select areas of Vermont. Sky's experience in New Orleans, and as a mediator, made him a natural for the job. I continued to manage my mother's properties, her finances, and her health care, all the while resenting every moment. I was not cut out to be a landlord, and it was hard to care for someone who was so ungrateful and angry.

We continued to look for another U.S.-based boat. We had learned about the Great Loop—a six-thousand-mile route that takes you (in our case) from Lake Champlain either north through the Richelieu River to the St. Lawrence or south down the Champlain Canal to the Erie Canal and west to the Great Lakes. From there, you make your way to Chicago, then to the Mississippi, down to and across the Gulf of Mexico where a canal takes you across Florida to the Intracoastal Waterway, and back north to Lake Champlain. We wanted to do it!

Research and planning and searching for a boat kept us busy and less depressed being stuck in Vermont. Then, success! We found a very cozy hand-built twenty-four-foot boat in Georgia. The original owner used her for fishing in the Atlantic off the coast of Florida, so we knew she was seaworthy enough for the Great Loop. We figured we could travel the one thousand miles up the Intracoastal Waterway to Vermont in six to eight weeks. I got my landlord and mother duties taken care of, knowing we could keep in touch via phone and email. In early April 2012, we were off.

But . . . that winter Sky had told me he was worried about his "brain health," feeling "old," and needing to do "brain exercises." We looked up "brain health" on the internet and found the things one needed to do to maintain a strong brain:

Mediterranean diet: check.

Regular exercise: check.

Strong social and emotional connections: check.

Regular mental stimulation: check.

No smoking or excessive alcohol use: check.

Healthy blood pressure, blood sugar, and cholesterol: check.

OK. Nothing to be done more than what Sky (and I) was already doing. This concern would pass.

But I noticed that Sky seemed to be more spaced out than usual and was having a hard time focusing and following through on tasks. Sky's laid-back personality was normally a pleasure to be around, but when he was stressed, it would manifest as spaciness and procrastination. I figured Sky was just stressed about his job, my mother, and whether or not we would be able to go on with our lives the way we wanted to. I figured getting on the boat would perk him up—so much to learn and do with a new boat with new systems, navigating on a waterway where neither of us had been before. He'd snap out of it.

And he did. What an adventure! The Intracoastal Waterway was nothing like the canals of France. Being parallel to the ocean, and open to the ocean periodically, we had to learn about tides. You couldn't just stop for the night and tie up on the side of the Waterway; you had to drop anchor at a safe place or pay to stay at a very expensive (compared to France) marina. It was fun and amazing to hang out with dolphins and feel the water move with the tides. It was strange not going ashore every day and not traversing locks. But we settled in and enjoyed the new challenges until one day in North Carolina when we hit bad weather.

We were in a section of the Waterway where the channel was narrow, and you could not get to land, as it was too shallow. There was a lot of boat traffic, and given that all the other boats on the Waterway were much bigger than we were, we were frequently tossed around in their wash as they passed us. I was at the stern, keeping my eye out for such boats and warning Sky, when the aft door came off its latch in the wind and slammed shut on my thumb. I pushed the door open and discovered that the last three-quarter inch of my thumb was dangling by a sliver of skin. I put it back together and held pressure on it while Sky called the Coast Guard. They came and rescued me in a Zodiac (a fast inflatable boat), which was able to get me to shore and onto the waiting ambulance, which took me to the nearest hospital, a half hour away. Sky was left on the boat to make his way alone to the town with the hospital—a trip of several hours in our small, slow vessel.

All's well that ends well, sort of: Sky got to the hospital just as I was being discharged. The ER doc had sewed the end of my thumb back on and said, "Let's hope for the best." No guarantees it would hold, or the bone would grow back, as it had been crushed. However, that was the end of our boating career until my thumb healed, so we headed back to Vermont.

We were both disappointed but also encouraged. We loved our little "rubber ducky" and felt she would be right for the Great Loop. We also needed to give her a name; I had happily scraped off the previous owner's name for her, but we'd learned it was bad luck if a boat didn't have a name. While I pondered names (and healed), Sky went off to France to bring *Antinous* to a marina where she could be sold. It was time to stay in the U.S., especially given that we had no idea how long my mother would live.

We chose the name *Iris*—a beautiful flower, the goddess of the rainbow, and a kind of fleur-de-lis, symbol of both New Orleans and France. Healed and settled, we headed back to *Iris* to resume our journey north. It was good to be back . . . until we had to cross the Albemarle Sound, the largest body of water we had encountered yet. Once we headed out, we could not see any land at all. It was my first experience like this, and once the west wind kicked up, I was petrified as *Iris* tossed about. Sky did an excellent job navigating, and after three frightening (for me) hours, we were safe in the Pasquotank River. From there until Norfolk, we were in the Dismal Swamp canal system, and I felt secure.

Once we reached Norfolk, I knew the Chesapeake Bay was next, and I didn't think I had the nerve to do it. But if I didn't, I also knew I wouldn't be able to do the Great Loop. It was a rough time as Sky and I discussed what to do. He really, really wanted to do it, so I left him to handle it alone and headed back to Vermont. He did an excellent job, handling *Iris* alone, finding places to anchor safely for the night, dealing with tides and winds. He said I wouldn't have liked it, so I knew I had made the right choice, though I watched yet another dream die.

Facing several weeks of bad weather that would make the open ocean crossing from northern New Jersey to New York City next to impossible for little *Iris*, Sky returned to Vermont to get the trailer, and brought her to the marina on Lake Champlain where we planned to spend the summer, having decided to sell our house. Time for more decisions.

Another bright idea: We decided to build a boat-on-land, also known as a tiny house on a trailer. With our house sold, *Iris* out as a Great Loop boat, New Orleans house unfinished but occupied by a friend looking out for it, we needed a place to live, and something to do. We set about researching and designing a tiny house, purchasing the trailer, and getting started. We would travel and do volunteer work. Perfect.

Then my mother broke her hip, and said, "Don't let them get me out of bed. I want to die." Even in her confusion and anger, she knew what she wanted. It took ten long weeks, but she finally died in mid-October 2012, just as we were doing the final work on the tiny house. As executor, I started to handle my mother's final affairs while Sky researched volunteer opportunities. If he wasn't busy, he still spent time being spaced out and ungrounded, but he was happy.

Off we went. We loved living in the tiny house, so basic, so simple, so portable. We took our time traveling to our first volunteer gig, which didn't work out. Neither did the second one, so we headed for New Orleans, where we found a place to park the tiny house on the top floor of a parking garage that was now an RV park.

We loved being back in New Orleans, hanging out with friends, working on our house when its occupant went away on business trips, playing disc golf, riding bikes, doing the usual music and food things. But Sky continued to space out enough that it began to make me mad—it felt like he was closing himself off from me. We had ongoing discussions about it, and Sky finally created a list of twelve "rules"—things he promised to himself, and to me, including:

- Pay attention—remembering is important.
- Stay flexible in mind and body.
- Make a place for everything and remember.
- Stay in touch especially when times are confusing.

* * *

Spring 2013 came, and with it, the intense heat of New Orleans. Time to move on—but to which boat? Perhaps it was time to look for property on Lake Champlain where we could keep *Iris*. Maybe we should look into electrifying *Antinous*, who still hadn't sold. Caught once again in a swirl of *What are we doing with our lives?* we made our way to Vermont in the tiny house and started to look for property. After a month's failure, we parked the tiny house and headed for France.

We loved being back aboard *Antinous*, but Sky continued to be off in his own world and was so stressed by big events, he would want to sleep for days. The canals and rivers were flooded, so we had to cool our heels for several weeks before we could get going. This sank Sky deeper into stress and spaced-out-ness. Finally, we got going—and, busy and less stressed, Sky returned to his usual cheerful, laid-back self. But I was worried.

In the fall, after listing *Antinous* with a boat broker, we returned to Vermont, found a property on Lake Champlain, bought it, and built yet another house. Would we finally be settled? I decided to go back to graduate school and found myself a part-time job. Once the house was done, Sky had no idea what to do with himself. He looked into volunteer work but found nothing that spoke to him. He was "disjointed" and "lost," and he just didn't seem to hear me at times. Was that willful or organic? Off he went to a hearing aid specialist, where he was tested and given hearing aids, which he hated and didn't want to wear.

Things seemed to be going from bad to worse. I was busy with school and work, but Sky mainly puttered around the house, did some hiking, designed a disc golf course in a nearby park, and spent time cruising around the lake on *Iris*. I was usually too busy to join him. Everything felt sad, and I was afraid of what might be happening. In the fall of 2014, Sky announced that he didn't want to live in Vermont, that he wanted to go back to New Orleans! Anything to make him happy, so we packed up our two cats and headed south. There was plenty to do there—the finish work was still not done, and in the meantime, we discovered that the cork flooring had buckled and needed to be replaced. Sky would have plenty to do, and I would commute back to Vermont for my part-time job. My classes were online, so I could do that from anywhere. By June, I had graduated and quit my job. It was a strange year, but it worked. Sky was happier, and seemed less spaced out.

Sky put *Iris* on the market, we found renters for our Vermont house and a house- and cat-sitter for New Orleans, and since no one was interested in *Antinous*, we headed back to France for the summer of 2015 with the plan to convert the diesel engine to electric and cover her roof with solar panels. Sky found a boat electrician outside of Amsterdam who could do the work, and we headed out on yet another boating adventure, this time going through France to Belgium and on to the Netherlands. It was exciting— and incredibly stressful. We were going places we had never been before, and we discovered that boating culture was very different in Belgium, and yet again even more different in the Netherlands.

Sky began making many mistakes as "captain"—losing the ability to land the boat properly, to go in and out of locks correctly, and to back the boat up right. He seemed to have lost his spatial sense, and I was scared and angry. On the one hand, he would acknowledge his spatial difficulties, but on the other hand, he denied that anything was wrong. Successfully moored outside of Amsterdam, with work commencing on *Antinous*, we headed back to the U.S.

Back in Vermont, we stayed for a couple of weeks to help Dana fix up her new condo. After ripping up the bedrooms'

wall-to-wall carpeting, Sky and Dana set about installing
new hardwood flooring. I was charged with painting the
living room walls. Simple tasks, right? Ones we had done
many times before. But as I carefully cut the edges and
painted the new colors, I listened to Sky and Dana arguing
about the flooring installation. "No," she'd say. "That's not
how it goes." While Sky could run the special flooring nail
gun, he could no longer figure out how to lay out the flooring so that the piece breaks were not near one another. In a
major reversal, Dana took charge of the project. I painted
through tears. Something was definitely wrong with Sky.

Once settled back into our house in New Orleans, Sky
found some compelling volunteer work with the court system. I breathed a sigh of relief. Surely his memory issues/
spaced-out-ness would go away now that he was so engaged
with something important. I focused on the home front:
gardening, cooking, knitting, reading, going for long walks
or bike rides. I did not want to allow myself to consider
that Sky might have dementia—I was still holding out for
blaming his problems on not paying attention. When the
family gathered for Thanksgiving in a place none of us had
been before, it was very noticeable that Sky was unable to
understand his new surroundings. Dana begged him to get
checked out: "If Jane was brave enough to have a colonos-
copy, you can get your brain evaluated!"

In January of 2016, I was moved by the plight of the
Syrian refugees fleeing their war-torn country, and I signed
up with a medical team charged with greeting the refugees
on the shores of Lesvos after they made their way across the
Aegean Sea. We cared for those hypothermic or injured, got
people dry clothing and cups of tea, and readied them for

the next phase of their journey. I was scared to leave Sky, and asked friends to keep an eye on him while I was gone. It was an amazing experience, but I was relieved to get home to Sky. He clearly was not any better.

In March, Sayer and his partner, Emma, came to visit. We had a fun week riding bikes, showing them the sights, taking in music and good food, and playing lots of disc golf. The weather was perfect, and they enjoyed the respite from the Vermont winter. On their last night, Sayer said they wanted to buy a house in Burlington, but felt they couldn't afford it. Would we be interested in helping them out? "How about a duplex?" I asked. "You two could live in one half, we could have the other half as our Vermont base." Great idea. It was agreed that Sayer and Emma would start to look at properties on their return, and if they found something they liked, I would come up and look at it.

I was relieved. Although I loved New Orleans, I knew something was seriously wrong with Sky. To live in a duplex next to Sayer and Emma brought me great comfort. If Sky really had dementia, I would have them to support me, plus Dana would be only forty-five minutes away. Things moved quickly: they found a suitable property, I made the trip to look at it, and we all agreed it was a good match for our criteria. We made an offer, it was accepted, and the closing took place at the end of April. The house was in serious need of renovation, but the four of us had the necessary skills. Sky and I would live there during the construction, moving from room to room and floor to floor as we demolished and rebuilt.

We were able to get the same woman who had house- and cat-sat for us the summer before in New Orleans, so with a clear conscience we headed north with our carpentry tools, some clothes, and a few kitchen things. With renters still in the house on Lake Champlain, we put it on the market and warned them they would need to find another place to live. Fortunately, with the Vermont real estate market being strong, we found a buyer right away. Phew. One house down. *Iris* sold. One boat down. Things were coming together.

Except for Sky. Not only was he having serious memory lapses, he was unable to do any carpentry work. He couldn't cut a straight line. He couldn't figure out angles. He became fearful that we would get hurt. He would stand and stare at the house, unable to engage. He couldn't stay on task. He said he was having a hard time finding words sometimes. That did it for him. He finally agreed to be tested.

First stop: before the memory center would see him, he had to see an internist to be tested for a multitude of conditions that might cause dementia, plus have an MRI. The blood tests were all negative; the MRI "inconclusive."

Second stop: a PET scan to image his brain.

Third stop: a visit with the memory center neurologist to discuss the findings.

On August 15, 2016, Sky was told he had "probable early stage Alzheimer's disease."

Once in the safety of our car, he said to me, "I think this is going to be harder for you than for me."

THE FIRST YEAR
August 2016–July 2017

SETTLING IN
TO A NEW REALITY

By **simple coincidence,** Sky and I left on a two-week trip to Europe the day after we received his Alzheimer's diagnosis. We had been busy renovating our new home all summer, living among the dust and construction, but the drywall guys said we had to vacate the premises for two weeks while they did their work.

We were excited to get back to *Antinous* and to test out the new electric motor system. We had no idea how fast Sky's illness would take away his various skills, so we hoped we would still be able to spend time on the boat. The weather wasn't great—high winds and rain—so we spent a lot of time cuddled up, reading, talking, crying, and being together. Twice the weather cleared, and we took *Antinous* out for a spin. It was very disappointing. The system did not work as expected. We consulted with the fellow who had done the work, and with the electric motor people, and we all eventually came to the conclusion that because *Antinous* was made of steel, the engine was simply too small for her weight.

With more bad weather in the forecast, we abandoned ship and headed for Paris. Over our years of canal cruising, we had spent a fair amount of time in Paris, so I was surprised that Sky could not navigate the Metro system, nor did he ever have any idea where we were in the city, how to read a map, or where our hotel was. Yet, when we went out for a meal or into a store, his French was impeccable.

We wandered the city streets, holding hands, talking, crying, wondering what was in store for us. Sky said, "I don't want to forget you, but mostly I don't want to forget myself." He became anxious about every little thing (and this was a guy who had never been anxious about anything before) and talked about his anxiety as "a whole-body feeling."

Before we knew it, we were back in Vermont, deep in the house renovation project. Sky abandoned any participation in it—which was fine—and set out to find "his people" and to educate himself about dementia. He read every book the library had on the subject, and ordered more. He began attending the local Memory Café—a once-a-month gathering for people with dementia and their loved ones. We tried a support group for couples with dementia, but it wasn't the right fit for us. We met with an estate lawyer to take care of our wills and our advance directives and create a trust for our finances. Sky visited the local memory care facility to check it out and find out what it cost. I opened a savings account and began to put aside any money I could in case the day came when I would have to pay for Sky's care. Sky found some volunteer work at a community bike shop, the community sailing center, and a local theater venue.

And he began to slip away. Because of his anxiety, he didn't want me to tell him anything "bad." So Sayer, Emma, and I handled the rest of the house renovations, and by the end of October we all had finally settled in to our dust-free surroundings.

I found I had little patience for this new Sky—I wanted my best friend back. I hated not being able to tell him anything and everything. I began to grieve each loss as it came along. I was sad and resentful.

To get out of my personal pity party, I asked Sky if there was anything he wanted to do while he still could—did he want to travel? Visit old friends? Yes, he did. He wanted to go skiing out West. He wanted to visit friends in New Orleans, the Pacific Northwest, and the Bay Area. So we made train reservations and headed out in February 2017.

I was excited, yet also scared. Would Sky get lost? Would he be able to handle all the new places we were staying? Would I have the energy to keep everything all together? We had traveled extensively over the years, but always in partnership. Now I had to be in charge. The trip was mostly fine. Sky enjoyed seeing people. He loved skiing and, amazingly, never got lost. He did struggle with finding the bathroom at night wherever we were, and did get lost once when he went out for a walk alone. Mostly, we had fun, but it was good to get home.

Sky got depressed that he might live too long. I got angry with myself for being impatient with him, resentful of him. I found a therapist—Sky said he didn't want one—but quit after a few sessions as it didn't seem to be making things any better for me. Sky's elderly aunt became ill, and we made several emergency trips to visit her outside of Philadelphia. Sky was unable to do any of the driving—he was too scared.

We discovered the Dementia Action Alliance and attended their annual conference in June in Atlanta. Sky was hoping to connect with other people with dementia, but had no luck. We were inspired by the major speakers, but the workshops were disappointing.

In July, Sky's aunt died. Her passing was peaceful and expected, but it made Sky think about his own death. That scared him. At the same time, our blog, which we had started in April, was getting a lot of notice, and we were on a local radio program. Sky would go back and forth between positivity—feeling like he was doing something important—and negativity—as his life was disappearing before his eyes.

In the announcement for our blog, we wrote:

> We started this blog as a way to erase the stigma attached to dementia and to increase understanding of the way it affects people on a day-to-day basis. People with dementia, and their loved ones, are not to be pitied or ignored, but to be treated with the full respect accorded to anyone, and with the understanding that they can meaningfully participate in life and in society despite their disability.

What follows are our blog posts from that first summer, which tell the story of the first year of Sky's diagnosis. Throughout this book, our posts have been lightly edited and occasionally rearranged for clarity but otherwise remain true to the originals.

* * *

[Note: You may notice that Sky often refers to himself as "demented," and you may be asking yourself, Isn't that considered a derogatory word? The word comes from the Latin demens, *meaning "out of one's mind." In the seventeenth century—long before dementia was a medical diagnosis—it was used to describe someone who was insane. Gradually, dementia became used to name what doctors had previously called "senility."*

Language has changed over time, and many offensive words have been dropped from our vocabulary. But just as other groups have embraced or reclaimed words for themselves that have been historically used in a derogatory way, some people with dementia refer to themselves as "demented." If they are describing themselves, it's fine. For the rest of us, it's best to say "person with dementia."]

SKY: WELCOME TO MY WORLD

Have you noticed?
these posts are
sometimes in order
and sometimes not.
some are longer,
some are shorter.
some might even begin to rhyme
others have slipped their anchors to time
WELCOME TO MY WORLD!

. . . .

SKY: TAKING THE TEST

In August 2016, Jane and I take our fateful first trip to the
memory center, a facility operated by the University of Vermont
Medical Center. Here's how the center describes what they do:

> "Memory loss can be a serious medical condition . . .
> or simply a recurring forgetfulness that affects many of us.
> To help patients understand their memory condition, the
> Memory Program at the University of Vermont Medical
> Center provides evaluation, diagnosis, and treatment of
> age-related memory disorders."

That sounds OK. I mean, they have some ways of reassuring
people what kind of memory loss they have. If my family
wants me to get checked out . . . what harm could it do?

And, in truth, my memory is not all that hot these days, but whose isn't at sixty-six years? You know, walk into a room and then stand there like a post wondering why, exactly, I'd wanted to go there? Most of us do that, right? Don't we? C'mon! I seem to remember always doing this, but then again, like I said, my memory today isn't quite as sharp as always.

I wonder if they do tune-ups at this place. Or establish a baseline and then do regular assessments or something. Might even be interesting in a way.

So, here we go . . .

On time, we make our way to the clinic. As we check in, I look over the other people in the reception room. They're a quiet group overall. Everyone's older than me except for a few who I guess are caregivers with their aged parents.

Jane and I are separated. We are each interviewed by a psychologist, and we are both asked about my skills of daily living: How am I doing at dressing myself, eating, getting myself to the toilet? Any car crashes or other trauma lately? If this is how they decide if I have a "serious medical condition," I'm probably in the clear.

Then I'm told there will be an hour-long neurological exam to test my cognitive and memory abilities. OK. This is when I rise and shine. I've always been a good tester in school, and now I'm feeling pretty confident about this one, clearly a major part of the assessment.

This test is when they sort me . . . *ace* it, then!

This I can do . . . these are my skills . . .

Sure enough, it's easy . . . (mostly).

"What am I holding?"

"Uh, that's a pen!"

"What is the weather today?"

"What season is this?"

Really?!?

This stuff is what they post on the walls for the droolers in so-called nursing homes!

How about: "What am I doing here?"

How about something at least a little challenging?

"Copy this drawing."

Easy.

"And this one."

Easy.

"And this one."

Easy.

"And this one."

Still easy, but getting harder.

"And this one."

Easy, but . . .

"And this one."

Uh-oh . . . impossibly 3D, all this detail . . . *shit* . . . It takes me three tries to get even close . . . hmmm.

After a few more hard ones: "Now, draw a clock."

Hah! I'm ready for this! I've learned that Alzheimer's people can't draw clocks for anything . . . and I'd practiced at home . . . absolutely no sweat! Now, how about some extra credit for confidence and speed?

Do I really need to be here?

She wants to know what this phrase means: "People in glass houses shouldn't throw stones." I'm sorely tempted to tell her one of my favorite jokes, the one about the jungle king that ends, tragically, "People in grass houses shouldn't stow thrones."

But something tells me this is not a great time to be a wiseass. After all, she is trying to evaluate my brain. I don't want her taking points off for a bad attitude.

Soon the test is almost over. My tester (a.k.a. staff psychometrist) tells me a long, involved story with numerous characters having numerous adventures that gets more and more long and involved. Of course, I'm expected to repeat it all back. Then a long list of numbers to memorize. More and more, until I'm falling on my face in frustration. For a break I get to count backward from one hundred by sevens.

Next, I'm instructed to fold a piece of paper lengthwise, set it on the floor, then pick it up and place it on the desk.

And for a grand finale, she wants to hear me tell her back her convoluted story of fifteen minutes ago.

Ouch!

SKY: PET SCAN AND DIAGNOSIS

After a week or two of fussing and wondering how I did taking the test, Dr. P. lets me know I did very well—"high average"—cryptically adding that had I taken the test several years ago, it probably would have been "superior." Now he recommends an additional test, a PET scan, to make a more conclusive diagnosis. I'd done so well on the neuropsychological testing (e.g., remembering the names for "comb" and "pen," among other things!) that he was looking for more data to make a clear diagnosis.

So, back to the hospital again for what turned out to be my favorite of the barrage of tests. (Not that anyone cares about my personal preference, but still.) I had to fast, no solid food or juice or *coffee* for the morning of the test. That wasn't so bad, but more interesting, they wanted me to "become a couch potato" for twenty-four hours before the actual test. No exercise. Walking only if necessary. Just chill out and relax.

Nice. Sure beats repeated blood drawing!

The idea was to check out my brain "at rest." Keeping with the quiet theme, the test took place in a dimly lit, secluded cranny of the hospital. The technician who came to get me spoke slowly and quietly as she led me through one corridor after another to the procedure room, calmly answering my many questions on the way. When we arrived, she motioned to a huge, overstuffed, very comfortable chair. I climbed in. Then she explained that she would start an IV and I was to rest, rest, rest for a while. She promised to come back after a time and wheel me into the scanner for the actual test. She told me how long these times would be, but in my relaxed and monitored state, I felt no need to remember them.

In due time, my guide returned and got me to my feet for the short walk—which kind of interrupted the mood—to the scanning machine itself. More techs were waiting to assist me onto the table that would slide into the machine that would scan my brain. The soft-spoken gals explained that at a certain time they would inject the contents of the IV bag into my bloodstream, and the machine would record how my brain handled it. The bag held a glucose solution with radioactive markers that the machine could track and evaluate how well the various parts of my brain were working.

Pleasant. Pleasant.

Back into the space-age machine. It's clanking now, in a soothing way. I drift off, into a nap.

* * *

A week later . . .

Dr. P. calls me into his office. This is it. Finally, he has all my ducks in a row.

> Neuropsychological testing: COMPLETE
> Neurological physical exam: COMPLETE
> Blood work screening: COMPLETE
> Personal neurological history: COMPLETE
> Family neurological history: COMPLETE
> Magnetic resonance imagery scan: COMPLETE
> Positron emission tomography scan: COMPLETE

Though we have a full half hour to meet, he gets right to the point: "I wish I had better news."

OK, I'm listening now!!

Leaning over his computer, he reads:

> There is hypometabolism most pronounced in the parietal and temporal lobes. To a lesser extent, there is hypometabolism evident within the frontal lobes also. Hypermetabolism of the posterior gyri more pronounced than that seen on the frontal lobes.
>
> There is also markedly decreased tracer uptake noted in the primary visual cortex of the occipital lobe.

"So, these are the data that the scan has detected," Dr. P. continues. "Hypometabolism means your brain is not utilizing the glucose as it should. This problem is manifested in several areas of your brain."

The conclusion:

Dr. P.: "I'm sorry to have to tell you this. The results of your PET scan are consistent with early stage Alzheimer's disease. It's not a slam-dunk diagnosis at this time. We will be following you over the months and years ahead to monitor your progress and keep an eye on things.

"I would estimate you have about eight to ten years, give or take."

"You mean, eight to ten good years . . . before . . ." I manage to mutter.

"Well, no. That would be lifetime."

A long pause. Dr. P. and I are each waiting for the other to say something. After I don't, he offers, "In the meantime, there are drugs available . . ."

. . . .

JANE: THE DIAGNOSIS

"The results of your PET scan are consistent with early stage Alzheimer's disease," says Dr. P., soothingly and solemnly.

Thank god, I say to myself. *I'm not going crazy. There* is *something wrong with Sky.*

I place my hand on Sky's arm and watch his deer-in-the-headlights look blossom.

These words might be soothing to me, but they sure as hell aren't soothing to Sky. He claims he remembers little from that day, but with significant short-term memory loss, what can you expect? Can't say as I remember that much either, some questions and answers between Sky and the doctor: "No, we can't predict anything." "Probably you have six to eight good years, maybe more, maybe less." Not really answers, then, mostly statements that could be said to anyone. Some discussion of medications, pros and cons, and whether it's worth trying one. Then we leave.

We leave to go home, holding hands on the way to the car, in the car before Sky starts driving, and most of the way home. Luckily, it's not far. Sky makes three phone calls—to his oldest friend, to his sister, and then to his daughter. He will tell his son later that day when his son gets home from work. I try and give him privacy for those phone calls. I stay in the house, alternately crying and rejoicing.

You may think it's cruel that I'm rejoicing. I'm happy—thrilled, even—that after several years of knowing something was not right, I now know what the problem is. For me, knowing gives me the opportunity to do something about the problem. Not knowing leaves me constantly wondering, fussing, trying this, suggesting that, only to leave both me and Sky confused and no closer to an answer.

Not that there is really anything for me to "do" now. This isn't a treatable disease like cancer or heart disease, where one can research treatments, make changes to lifestyle, look for a second opinion or the best research hospital. There is nothing to be done here. I don't even need to educate myself about the disease, as I spent several years working in a memory care unit in a nursing home. I know about Alzheimer's and other forms of dementia. I know the kind of care that is necessary as someone reaches the stage of needing institutional or full-time help.

So, for right now, all there is for me to do is to learn patience. It won't be easy.

ALZHEIMER'S CANYON:
A Parable in Eleven Episodes

In addition to his blog posts about real-life experiences, Sky wrote a more fantastical story about a regular guy, innocently traveling life's highway, who unexpectedly ends up in an exceedingly bizarre place called Alzheimer's Canyon. The eleven episodes were originally posted between April 2017 and February 2018 but have been scattered throughout this book, "loosing the tethers of time," as Sky liked to say. It may be fiction, but the story holds plenty of truth about the journey Sky found himself on.

ALZHEIMER'S CANYON:
The Arrival

WTF? This rutted off-ramp isn't on the map, or the GPS either. And actually, there is no choice: The huge reflective barrier informs me that the highway ahead is closed. Road ends. This grubby detour is my only way out of here. Sure enough, there's Dr. P. wearing a highway patrol outfit, directing traffic (me), making sure I get off the interstate, now.

Kind of a pain in the ass, because I'd been making good time up on the four-lane across the high country. The driving has been easy—spectacular, at times. Wide open country, mesas, buttes, purple mountain majesty. All that stuff. The road signs out here tell you the altitude when you enter the next town, and I've been enjoying how I've been effortlessly climbing up and up without any perceptible strain on the vehicle. Nice.

But now this detour. WTF, indeed. I mean, planning my trip, I knew that Alzheimer's Canyon was in the area, but I just wasn't all that interested. It's an old-person destination, right? And whatever else I am, I sure don't see myself as elderly.

But, again, there is no choice. I know Dr. P. isn't going to let me camp here on the interstate exit. He's got to keep the traffic flowing. Dr. P. gives me a friendly but authoritative wave as I pass by.

It's only as I'm gaining speed on the narrow, bumpy, pathetic excuse for an off-ramp that I notice the other highway signs: one way; no u-turns.

I checked, and this road I'm on isn't on my fold-up map. The Canyon itself is on the map, though, and if I read it right, the thing is phenomenally huge, especially compared to the skinny track I'm on to get in there. This approach road is pleasant enough, if a little lonesome. Good thing it's posted one-way traffic because there really isn't room for anyone getting out this way.

Finally, a huge billboard lets me know that the AC Visitors Center is just ahead. Also, parking lots 1–275.

A.C. Interactive Visitors Center ↗

"Good afternoon, how can we help today?" asks the smiling AmeriCorps worker behind the counter.

"Well, I guess I could use a map or a guide or something," I respond.

"Of course! We have these guides to the Canyon itself. Also accommodations . . . or will you be camping in your RV?"

"Ughh, I don't have an RV, just my own little car. I only got here because of a detour on the interstate."

"Yes, well, we have options here for you. For instance, you could try the homeless encampment in Area B, past the dumpsters. They may have room for you under a piece of plastic. They're always getting new sheets in over there. Or, if you prefer, the hotel may have a spot. It's $12,000 a month, or maybe there's a waiting list? I don't really know . . . ?"

"Actually, I was trying to work some of the interactive exhibits over there, and I think they might be broken . . . or maybe I'm not running them right?"

"Oh, you're fine. They don't do anything unless you're a caregiver." The attendant grins. "And, unless you've got Grandma out there in your RV, I don't guess you're a caregiver. So, since you aren't, I guess you're maybe a sufferer, and we really don't have anything for sufferers."

"But I don't have an RV . . ."

"If you're in the market, we have quite a good selection of gently used motor homes right now in Area E."

"Can I just look at the Canyon while I'm here?"

"Of course! That's what this guide is all about!"

"Oh, yeah," I answer. "I saw that one and I couldn't make *any* sense out of it. The only English words on it said, 'Start Here.'"

"Exactly! It tells you everything you need to know!"

"'Start here'?"

"Sure, sir."

"But . . . where?"

"Right where you are!"

"But, wait, how do I find the overlook, the vista, whatever?"

"Don't worry, you already found us. You're all set now."

She's grinning again, but I'm getting irritated with this whole Alice-in-Wonderland routine.

"Look, have you even got a guide in English?"

"Sir, of course it's in English. You read it yourself."

"No, no, no!! You've got a big pile of typos here, young lady. See, it just says 'Start Here' and the rest of the map is BLANK! No trails, no landmarks. Nothing!! I can't even use my compass. It's totally useless!!"

"Sir, if you're anxious, I can get you a prescription. In the meantime, you may want to get started."

"Started doing fucking *what*?!" Man, I'm ready to be out of this place.

"Well, sir, everyone's path is different. We can't predict what yours will be like . . . except that it's all downhill from here . . ."

SKY: DRUGS

Dr. P. barely skips a beat after letting me know my probable diagnosis—*Likely early stage of Alzheimer's dementia, with mild cognitive impairment*—before launching into his offerings for "treatment."

The quotation marks here indicate sarcasm, because there is no treatment.

No Treatment. No Treatment. No Treatment. No Treatment.

Despite huge efforts, Alzheimer's disease (AD) remains incurable, progressive, and fatal. There are no drugs to stop the progress of the deterioration or to build back brain capacity.

Dr. P. explained in his kindly, respectful manner that he would like to put me on Aricept, the most commonly prescribed drug for Alzheimer's. The drug "works" by changing the chemistry of the brain, adding cholinesterase inhibitors to increase acetylcholine levels in the brain to hopefully slow down the process of neuron decay and death.

Aricept was one of the first drugs approved by the FDA for Alzheimer's "treatment." (Now there are four, most of which hope to achieve results with the same strategy as Aricept.) The original tests, as well as some follow-ups to verify Aricept's efficacy, were paid for by the major drug manufacturers. These tests resulted in broad claims about slowing the progress of AD as well as reducing the extent of cognitive problems. Later, in 2000, a major study was conducted in Great Britain to evaluate the cost effectiveness of Aricept. The study meant to confirm that Aricept had a place in their National Health system of AD care.

Double-blind tests were administered to hundreds of people who had mild to severe Alzheimer's, using Aricept or a placebo. The results were discouraging to say the least:

There was a very small (statistically insignificant) difference in scores between the two groups on the standard neurological assessment. There was virtually no difference between the groups as to when the people with Alzheimer's needed nursing home care.

Basically, the study found that prescribing Aricept was a waste of government money. They urged researchers to explore other approaches than cholinesterase inhibitors, the centerpiece of Alzheimer's pharmacology.

At best, 50 percent of people with Alzheimer's who take the drug don't experience any benefit at all. And the "benefit" extends only to a possible slowing down of some of the disease's symptoms. There is *no* reversal of the rate of decline, and *no* alleviation of losses and damage, and *no* deviation of the course of this disease until it leads to my death. Of course, I might be lucky and die of something else first!

So, pretty much, the drug is recommended because it *might* do *something*. Chances are less than fifty-fifty that there will be any change at all. If it does do something, will I or anyone else even notice? To top it all off, trials demonstrated that any effects tend to wear off after six to nine months, although occasionally results lasted longer. To accommodate all these possibilities, the social worker at the memory center advised that the drug regimen was "lifetime."

I'm not at all sure that the drug is the right choice, but I am way too stunned by the diagnosis to have a discussion at this point. I decide to give the meds a try. The doctor tells me that I will take a limited dose for a few weeks. Then, if I tolerate the drug, I should double the dosage.

Aricept is cheap, four dollars a month, due to some kind of buying program at Hannaford, a local supermarket chain. At the pharmacy I feel like a doofus signing all the "necessary forms" with the staff there. This is the first time in my sixty-six years that I've had prescription medicine for anything besides an infection or as a painkiller. The people at the pharmacy are all very nice and seem happy to take me under their wing. I suppose they know my condition from my prescription (duh) and are giving the Alzheimer's patient extra slack.

I head home and dutifully take my pills at the assigned times and await the results. Will I be one of the lucky few who notice a change?

Short answer: Yes!

Longer answer: It's a change for the worse.

After a few days, I've become queasy 24-7. I eat dribbles of banana and bread many times a day and hope I can keep them down. When I go into any building, I first locate the bathroom in case this is where the vomiting will start. My head is fuzzy, my stomach fluttery, I'm generally out of it all day and all night. I just want to sleep all the time. I'm ready to get over the hump and become acclimated to the drug. Instead, it gets steadily worse.

A phone call to Dr. P. gives me the OK to drop the Aricept, and in a few days I get my regular life back. Now I take daily doses of Vitamin B Complex and CBD oil, and I feel fine.

* * *

[Note from Jane: For those of you who have been pregnant, Sky's constant nausea and tiredness reminded me of *the first trimester . . . eating strange things just to keep something down, and generally feeling worthless. Happily, he didn't have to wait three months to feel better!]*

. . . .

JANE: **HOW CAN I HELP?**

At some point in our lives (and probably more than once), we will be told by a friend that they (or their partner, parent, child, or other loved one) have been diagnosed with a serious, maybe even life-limiting, condition.

How do we respond?

I've got some ideas:

When your friend tells you of this diagnosis, **do** listen, and respond with empathy. It's OK to say anything from "That really sucks" to "I'm so sorry" and, if you're in person, offer a hug. Let them cry. Let them just be with what they are telling you.

After they have told you their story, **do** ask, "How can I help?" Everyone is different and will want different things from their friends, and that need will probably change over time. Ask them how is the best way to stay in touch: phone calls, email, texts, snail mail, in-person visits? Then **do** what they ask of you. Do they want meals brought in? Help with household tasks? Childcare? Pet sitting/dog walking? Lunch dates? Long walks? Just ask. They will know best what they need.

If they ask you to visit, **do** visit! Keep it short and specific, and keep it fun. Go for a walk; go out for coffee, lunch, or a drink; sit in a park or other beautiful place; take in a concert, play, movie, or sports event. Your friend is still your friend. What did you like to do together in the past? Do it now! Just know that it may be different for your friend—they may tire easily, may need to go home sooner than planned, or may need to have you leave if they're not feeling well. Remember, this is about their needs, not yours.

Do ask their care partner how you can best support them. Even though they may not physically have the condition, they live with it every day, and it can be physically and emotionally draining. Just as with your friend (above), plan to do something fun with their care partner—or offer to stay with your friend while their care partner goes out and does something fun on their own or with another friend.

Do not offer advice about "cures," special diets, herbal remedies, alternative health choices, or anything else you've read on the internet. Your friend and their care partner have already spent plenty of time on the internet and may even have sought a second opinion or advice from a major medical center. They have done their research and made their choices. Just listen. And for heaven's sake, **do not** tell them what a gift this is for them.

Do face your own mortality. If your friend's diagnosis brings up your own fear of illness and death, deal with it. Seek out another friend (**do not** discuss your personal concerns about this with your friend who has the illness or their care partner; they have enough to deal with) or a clergy person or therapist.

If your friend has dementia, **do** be prepared for them to change. They will not always be your same old friend in outward appearance. But, deep inside, they will still be your same old friend. They may no longer be comfortable leaving home, or may not be able to. They may not remember you. **Do** visit anyway. Your visit will bring them happiness. Sing or play music together. Look through photo albums or beautiful coffee table books. Read to them. Hold hands. Laugh. Offer to stay with them while their care partner runs errands, goes out for lunch, or takes a nap.

Do not assume your friend's dementia (or other illness) will be the same as your grandparent/parent/cousin/friend/partner who has/had the same condition. As the saying goes, once you've seen one person with dementia, you've seen one person with dementia. Everyone's path is different.

Do keep checking in with your friend and their care partner about what they need right now. And, above all, **do not** disappear from their lives. You are important!

SKY: NIGHTTIME TROUBLES

So, here's another not so pleasant aspect of Alzheimer's: trying to kill my wife. For several months now, once or twice a week, in the middle of the night, I have half-surfaced from horrible nightmares. The nightmares are truly terrifying, too terrifying to remember them all. Their themes are the same though. Something horrible is after me, and I have to fight back. My screams are reported to be blood-curdling. Worst is my strategy to actually fight back, hard, with Jane playing the role of the monster. So far, I've inflicted just scratches, but it's getting worse.

Jane is not pleased.

This morning at 2:12 a.m. I was catching my breath, sorting out my dream world from my waking one. I mentally went through my bedside table looking for sharp things, screwdrivers, or other weapons. None, thank goodness. I will keep this area clean.

Sleep is no longer my trusted friend.

But what about these dreams?

For over twenty-five years now I've been paying attention to my dreams, since I learned that by paying attention, I can almost always learn something from the time I spend in my dream world. My guide to this world, the Rev. Jeremy Taylor, insists that dreams come to us "in the service of health and wholeness."[1] In other words, there is no such thing as a "bad dream." If a dream is scary, it is trying to get our attention. If a dream is scary and repetitive, it is trying harder to get our attention.

I have tried to pay attention to whatever the evil dream thing is like. Sometimes I remember glimpses of a creature attacking me, but more often the killer is vague and hidden, and deadly.

Did someone say "Alzheimer's"?

I'm afraid these dreams are another way of saying, "Enough with the denial, Sky. The monster is really real. It will jump out at you unexpectedly. This thing is going to take your full attention. It will shake you to your core. Sometimes it will hurt you. Yet you will still always be you."

---

1. Taylor, "Group Work with Dreams" in Dreams: A Reader on the Religious, Cultural, and Psychological Dimensions of Dreaming, ed. by Kelly Bulkeley (New York: Palgrave Macmillan, 2001).

SKY: **WEAR AND TEAR**

More signs of wear and tear on those well-trodden nerve highways up there . . .

Up there? Where?

In my brain, of course.

OK, take this turn of phrase:

"Not unlikely east of the Green Mountains."

Part of a basic Vermont weather forecast, right?

Well, I can actually remember a time not long ago when I understood this phrase in a different way than I do now. Before, it was just a simple, descriptive comment that made perfect sense, no big deal. Now, I find myself unfolding my personal mental map almost every time I hear it. I orient the map, pointing east the correct way, and work out the "uns" and "nots." Then I'm able to see the meaning behind the phrase and move along.

I don't know the neuro-scientific explanation for my internal map project, but it really does feel like my carefully constructed ways of moving and arranging information efficiently inside my brain now need some major re-grooving.

The good news is I've been mostly successful, though often slower so far, at deciphering this strange language. "East of the Greens" now takes under three seconds. Not bad.

Bad news is (again) that this is as good as it will get from here on. Sadly, it becomes easier and easier to imagine a time when I won't be able to make sense of it at all.

And, when that time comes, I just hope that no one suggests that I hop in the car!!

SKY: REVERIE

Like a lot of people, I blunder through life, dividing my time among three familiar worlds: The Now, The Past, and The Future.

These days, I bounce, sometimes awkwardly, among the Big Three. I wonder if my recent diagnosis isn't cranking up the intensity. Like, today I found myself standing around somewhat blankly in the kitchen, a little light-headed and spacey. Oh, did I forget to eat lunch again? All of a sudden I realized I was ravenous, and, thrilled, I quickly put together (and savored) the meal I'd missed.

Delicious! As usual, returning to the Present presents unexpected presents! This time a meal to be savored.

As I finished my simple meal, my mind wandered back in time to the eating habits of my long-dead—and neurologically impaired—father, Charles. His culinary preferences included Ring Dings, Karo syrup straight out of the bottle, and black "coffee" made with Sanka and warm water from the sink.

In addition to his unusual dietary habits, my father lived with a severe case of multiple sclerosis and was in a wheelchair for a third of his life. Family and many friends were always cooking or bringing him special, healthy, and delicious foods, which he would dutifully eat, but he'd just as soon have one of his old favorites, like a grilled marshmallow sandwich on Wonder Bread.

Charles was a hero in our family and in his broader community for his eventual acceptance and embrace of his deteriorating condition. He was able to find the love beneath the pain and sorrows. Myself, I didn't do so well with the process . . . at all. I was mostly uncomfortable with his decades-long decline into quadriplegia. It was hard to share (or to resist!) his twinkle, especially in the intimate moments, like when I was feeding him. If I was around at all, I remained in a more or less constant, sullen funk at all of the losses and things we would never do together.

Now, many years later, I'm more able to appreciate the gift life is offering me to try again, this time with my own decline. Will I be able to find a place of acceptance and peace, as my father finally did?

And off I drift into the Future . . . preparing myself for a nightmare of forgetting.

Today I learned something interesting: there's more out there besides the Big Three for my mind to wander in. Yes, like where was that mind before I realized I was hungry? And what was my route from pondering the Past to imagining a wreck of a Future?

It almost seems like Alzheimer's provides a kind of neutral ground to hang out in without necessarily being Present. I've visited this place a few times already and expect to be back. Not good, not bad.

Detached . . . a safe place to observe.

SKY: A BAD DAY IN BURLINGTON

I planned on a quiet, relaxed morning, the start of a day and night on my own. Jane left town on a business trip, so I'll be on my own, usually a good time.

Sure enough, I'm up early and completely enjoying the clear quiet of a winter morning, a calm that penetrates even into my home in the center of Burlington—Vermont's biggest city.

But then, my peaceful, calm morning is ruined . . . by something. Something must have happened because now I'm a quivering ball of anxiety. I'm thinking about all the things to do. Some I *must* do . . . others are optional. Planning ahead, I've written all these down, just in case. But what, in fact, happened? What jerked me from my happy day to wallowing in my options? I know the answer, but I don't want to admit it: *I don't remember* what happened! Maybe something mysterious inside my brain where my 100 billion neurons are under attack. Or maybe something else that I have, so far, completely forgotten . . .

Time to get a grip and try some things. Today is Saturday, so the comedy shows on NPR might be worth a visit. They are, but then they're over. A friend calls to see if we might get together for lunch today. Oh no, can't do that: I'm meeting my daughter, Dana, and then off with her to a health care rally. Cool!

But wait, wait . . . we are running out of time. I haven't heard from her, and she's supposed to arrive late morning. I call, no answer, text, ask where she is, remind her of the rally. She takes a few minutes to respond.

Wisely, she calls. Also, wisely, she tells me I have the wrong date. I've got the schedule right, but TOTALLY THE WRONG DAY! This is all supposed to happen tomorrow instead. Shit!!

Though talking with Dana calms me down some, for some reason I don't let on how scattered I feel. I'm bouncing down a decrepit bobsled track. But it's not fun. The run hasn't been maintained. There's potholes and patches and jagged ice. I'm getting beat up just trying to maintain a semblance of emotional control. Holy fuck, where does all this come from?

Searching for *soothing*, I get domestic and heat up yesterday's soup that I liked so much and start some sunflower seeds for toasting. Then, all my options crowding against each other, I crave getting outside, so I shut down the stove and pack up Jane's package for the post office. Not sure of their hours, I do remember that they have shortened hours on Saturday. And, because of holidays, the package *must* be mailed today. So I go there first. Anxious still, the first thing I do at the PO is check the hours and sigh (loudly) with relief that they stay open 'til four (or five) on Saturdays. Good! I can relax.

Feeling a little more on top of it, I go inside the (heated) lobby. I'm stunned to see the Closed sign on the door leading to the service windows. A discreet sign informs the public that the windows close at 1 p.m. on Saturdays.

And I lose it. I check to see if there might be someone . . . anyone . . . in the building. There isn't.

I am fucked. Stupid. I DON'T WANT TO BE LIKE THIS!

Thank goodness this is a time of tears because here come some more . . .

I'm starting to pull my sniveling self together to ride back home when I hear a scream from Church Street, nearby. Then another. Running feet. More screams. It sounds like people having a harder day than mine. As I make my way over there, I see a group of maybe two dozen women holding signs: panic, scream, too much, panic. They pass around a bullhorn, and each person says a sentence or two about another unbelievable outrage expected from the incoming presidential administration. After each one speaks, all the women scream and run in terror, waving their signs. It was a little funny around the edges, but to me, the screams conveyed pure horror.

At the end, the woman with the bullhorn shouted the question, "What can we do so we don't have to scream?" A popular answer: "Fight back!"

That's what I need to do . . . *Fight back!* How? What is it, now, really, that I'm fighting?

I can start with finding a way to overnight Jane's package that I was entrusted to ship. Wonder if the extra charges can count as a medical expense?

. . . .

SKY: BRAIN HAT

About my fashion statement over there on the right . . .

For a couple of months now I've been sporting this hat, knitted by Jane. Every day I get comments. "Hey, that looks like a brain." "Love your hat, man!" And my favorite so far: "Psssst! Your brain is showing." Most comments toss the ball back into my court, giving me an opportunity to respond. Do I laugh and keep going? Do I stop and chat?

The hat is a pretty good indicator of how strong and confident and engaged I'm feeling. In fact, the hat has opened up some very interesting conversations. At the very least, it's good for eye contact and a good laugh. Once, feeling strong, I responded, "Actually, it's my Alzheimer's hat. I've recently learned that I have Alzheimer's, and the hat is giving my brain support."

Then the other person grins and says, "My wife has Alzheimer's. She's at home. Would you like to see a picture of her?"

"Of course!"

"See, she's very happy."

"Wow. She looks it," I say. And she really does. Something about her eyes conveys to me a presence, a steady strength that's hard to describe in words.

Could this be the Bond of the Demented?

Ten minutes later . . .

I'm getting another like for my hat. Energized, I repeat the line that just clicked so well. "Actually, it's my Alzheimer's hat. I've recently learned that I have Alzheimer's, and the Hat is giving my brain support."

This time, before I can finish my sentence, my liker is staring at her shoes, muttering, "Humff. Interesting . . ." and then barrels off down the sidewalk without a backward glance.

Hmmmm.

* * *

[Note from Jane: Want to make your own brain hat? Find the pattern at studioknitsf.com/how-to-knit-a-brain-hat-for-halloween. Making the hat is easy, but the I-cord for all the twirly brain parts is, shall I say, pretty boring but must be done—as well as sewing it all on. Be creative about your hat—make it any color(s) that you wish! Note: I made the hat with a circular needle (the pattern calls for double-points). Use whatever you're most comfortable with. Now it's time to make Sky one in cotton—I do hope spring will arrive soon!]

. . . .

SKY: THE END OF NATURE

Bill McKibben, one of my personal heroes, has emerged as a worldwide advocate for ending the human species' addiction to fossil fuels. With his groundbreaking book *The End of Nature*, published in 1989, he became the first to point out to a general audience the dangers and hidden costs of our addiction. Now, almost thirty years later, McKibben has become a rock star for the climate. He describes his schedule as "frenetic," traveling (primarily by plane) to speak to groups small and (mostly) large about the ways we, as a species, are fouling our nest. At rallies and protests he is relentless with the latest statistics and horrifying stories of a planet in serious trouble.

The End of Nature has a whole different tone. McKibben manages to include plenty of disturbing data—quite an accomplishment, since scientific study of climate instability was in its infancy then. But the overall tone of the book is remarkable, quiet and poignant as McKibben reflects on his theme. Basically, he notes that while the American Dream of Wilderness and New Land has been long dead, our parallel Dream of Endless Economic Growth, fueled by endless fossil-based energy, is still going strong even as producing this energy becomes more and more problematic.

Building, maintaining, and expanding this parallel dream has forever changed our world—and specifically, our idea of nature. In our selfishness, we have "blindly, crudely, but effectively" rewritten the laws of nature, writes McKibben:

> If the sun is beating down on you, you will not have the comfort of saying, 'Well, that's nature.' Or if the sun feels sweet on the back of your neck, that's fine but it isn't nature. A child born now will never know a natural summer or a natural autumn, winter, or spring. Summer is going extinct, replaced by something else that will be called 'summer.' This new summer will retain some of its characteristics—it will be hotter than the rest of the year, for instance, and the time of year when crops grow—but it will not be summer, just as even the best prosthesis is not a leg.[2]

How pervasive these new laws will be is literally up in the air. We have changed the atmosphere so radically, and continue so relentlessly, that the outlook is more than a little bleak.

Amyloid plaques and tau tangles are rewriting the laws in my brain every day and every night. No one knows when or why this rewrite began, but the outcome is less in doubt.

---

2. Bill McKibben, *The End of Nature* (New York: Anchor Books, 1989), 59.

As the Alzheimer's Association puts it:

> During this preclinical stage of Alzheimer's disease, people seem to be symptom-free, but toxic changes are taking place in the brain. Abnormal deposits of proteins form amyloid plaques and tau tangles throughout the brain, and once-healthy neurons stop functioning, lose connections with other neurons, and die.[3]

There is no known way to stop or slow down the progress of the disease, or to reverse any of the escalating damage to my brain neurons. The new laws are strict, if sometimes subtle. Simply said, I will be dealing with the effects of Alzheimer's every day until I stop breathing. As with *The End of Nature,* some of these are likely to be delicate and understated shifts in my mind. Others will be unmistakable, like hurricanes and sea level rise, nightmares and paranoia.

I have no idea how this will play out, but I plan on paying attention.

---

3. Alzheimer's Association, "Alzheimer's Disease Fact Sheet," 2.

ALZHEIMER'S CANYON
Episode 2

That's it! Enough with this crazy place, and crazier young lady. I stomp out of the so-called "Interactive Visitors Center" as quick as my legs will take me. When I calm down a little, I notice I've still got the worthless "guide" in my hand. And, of course, it's still blank. It wouldn't be so bad, if they didn't pretend to be giving out useful information only to slap you in the face with that blank page. Ugh!

I don't know where I am, and I'm not even in the Canyon yet. (At least I don't think I am.)

Wait, What? There's a restaurant, or a snack bar, or something. I've used up all my road food on this insane detour, and I'm hungry.

The restaurant looks a little more organized than that Visitor Center. They have a menu posted outside and the menu even has writing on it. Ha ha!! Wonder if it's gonna be pricey . . .

Let's see . . . Oooh, prix fixe. It is going to be fancy, but what the hell . . . I have a feeling that some comfort food will go down real good about now.

Kinda different. But then again, what isn't

THE ALZHEIMER'S CAFÉ
Menu

APPETIZER
Un Tangle d'Amyloid
thinly sliced, with choice of three in-house-prepared sauces:
a Libido Reduction —or—
a Sense of Direction Reduction —or—
for the less adventurous, a Smell/Taste Reduction

SALAD COURSE
Piles of Walnuts, Avocado, Kale & Salmon
with tau dressing, generously dusted with turmeric
& drizzled with dark chocolate

MAIN COURSE
Piles of Walnuts, Avocado, Kale & Salmon
with tau dressing, generously dusted with turmeric
& drizzled with dark chocolate

DESSERT
Piles of Walnuts, Avocado, Kale & Salmon
with tau dressing, generously dusted with turmeric
& drizzled with dark chocolate

around this place? Plus, I'm not getting any less hungry. Time to eat.

The maître d' meets me at the door. He's all in white, head to toe, very classy.

"Welcome to the Alzheimer's Café, sir. Do you have a reservation?"

"Well, no, this was an unplanned trip." Looking around and seeing no one, I ask, "Are you really open?"

"But of course, sir. We are *always* open!"

"It's just that . . . I don't see anyone else . . ."

"Yes, yes, quite a few went down today," he lets me know with a wink and a grin. Kind of an oily grin. The kind of oily grin that doesn't inspire a "Wait, what?"

"Will you be dining with us this evening, sir?"

I must look like an idiot, travel-worn and rumpled, standing in this fancy starched-white palace. Does the maître d' sense my discomfort?

"Sir, if you are concerned about a dress code, do not trouble yourself. We serve everyone here. We will meet you where you are. Please, have a seat. We'll take it from here . . . sir."

As you might imagine, the food is as strange as everything else in this special place, but I'm a good boy and eat what I am given. Soon a group of three joggers shows up. With nothing else to do, I stare at them, and try to discern. Something is off about them, but it takes me a while to figure it out. The men are just in from a run. I hear something in their talk about the ten-mile mark. Another mentioned the upcoming ACM, Alzheimer's Canyon Marathon.

That's it! These guys are marathoners, at least in their spare time. And they are *old*. But their bodies—totally ripped!! All three have the lanky, sinuous build of the serious long-distance runner. On top of that, they sport sharply defined muscles . . . everywhere.

Ever since I watched Jack LaLanne on TV as a kid, I've been amazed about old people with real physical skills. As an elementary-aged nerd, it was hard to ignore the images of SuperMen everywhere.

Just two highlights of Jack's accomplishments (check out Wikipedia for a more complete list):

in 1959
Jack's age: 45
Sky's age: 9

Jack sets a world record by doing 1,000 pushups and 1,000 chin-ups in one hour and twenty-two minutes.

in 1974
Jack's age: 60
Sky's age: 24

Jack swims from Alcatraz Island to Fisherman's Wharf with his hands tied together, towing a 1,000-pound boat.

Jack LaLanne was a showman and businessman. He sold elixirs to counteract the "pollution" in the Western diet. Most memorable for me was the way that he came into my life through the television, demonstrating and sharing his exercise program with the world, one TV at a time. Handsome, healthy, and friendly, he was a "regular guy" who happened to be bulging with muscles and was prepared to tow heavy boats while swimming in the ocean handcuffed.

He was convinced that good diet and exercise (*lots* of exercise) were the key to a long, healthy, and happy life:

> *Dying is easy. Living is a pain in the butt. It's like an athletic event. You've got to train for it. You've got to eat*

right. You've got to exercise. Your health account, your
bank account, they're the same thing. The more you
put in, the more you can take out. Exercise is king and
nutrition is queen: together, you have a kingdom.[4]

He also subscribed to the unfortunate concept of blaming people
living with Alzheimer's for bringing on their conditions:

I know so many people in their eighties who have
Alzheimer's or are in a wheelchair or whatever. And I say
to myself, "I don't want to live like that. I don't want to
be a burden on my family. I need to live life. And I'd hate
dying; it would ruin my image."[5]

Sadly for Jack, his "kingdom" proved mortal after all. He died in
January 2011, aged 96, of pneumonia. But his legacy lives on in his
"acolytes" everywhere, who plan on outwitting death and "disease"
with supplements and sit-ups. Good luck with that.

---

4. Quoted in Andrew Siegel, MD, Finding Your Own Fountain of Youth: The Essential Guide to
Maximizing Health, (Paul Mould, 2008), 191.
5. Quoted on Wikipedia, https://en.wikipedia.org/wiki/Jack_LaLanne; original source unknown.

JANE: THE MYTH OF THE FOUR THINGS

The Alzheimer's Association, AARP, and just about every health care practitioner we've run into these days has touted four things as a way to "age well," improve brain health, and keep you from getting dementia:

- Spend time with people/don't let yourself get isolated: find meaningful paid or volunteer work and hang out with people you love.
- Get some exercise—aerobic, several times a week: walking, biking, running, swimming, etc.
- Eat right, preferably a diet rich in plant foods: fruit, veggies, whole grains, nuts, legumes, fish—think Mediterranean diet.
- Keep your brain active with reading, puzzles, hobbies, and other mental challenges.

Right.

Given that Sky has done these four things the whole thirty-two years I have known him, that ain't necessarily so, Joe.

Everyone should be doing these four things, but they are no guarantee that you or your loved one will not get dementia. They're a recipe for a happy and healthy life, but you still might get cancer or heart disease, have a stroke, be hit by a bus crossing the street or, heaven forfend, get Alzheimer's.

There are no guarantees in life. The unexpected can happen at any moment. But, for some reason, we Americans think that if we exercise, eat right, meditate, pray, stay informed, and keep our minds active, we will be protected from death or disability.

Nope. Guess what. We all die. Life is 100 percent fatal.

It's best not to do these four things out of fear, but out of joy. Life is better if we feel good. Exercising and eating well help us feel good. Staying engaged in meaningful activities and spending time with our friends help us feel good. Let's do it! Live in the satisfaction that comes from doing these things, not out of panic or dread of the unknown. We cannot know for sure what will happen to us. Focus on living, focus on the now, and live a rich life while you can.

. . . .

SKY: STUPID

The other day I did something that left me feeling stupid.

I know, breaking news, right?

We all do "stupid things" every day. I know I do, always have.

Yet it's different now, somehow.

Here is what happened . . .

After playing bridge to exhaustion, I'm staggering to the door when I notice a briefcase on the floor. Memory circuits start firing, and as I stand there, swaying slightly, I'm recalling a few of the many times when I've spotted Sayer heading off to work in the early morning. Me, drinking my coffee in bed, and Sayer, on the outside, hauling his briefcase.

His briefcase is distinctive. It's slim (in a European style, perhaps) and Sayer carries it casually slung over a shoulder with a strap. Cool.

For some reason I choose this moment, staring at the briefcase, to mention how I like his briefcase. There is a short silence, then Sayer answers in a very even tone, "Um, that's Emma's briefcase?" And a low-to-medium wave of shame (somewhat disproportionate to misidentifying the briefcase) passes over. I resume my trajectory toward the door, muttering like a drunkard about how of course I knew the difference between the bags.

Stupid 1!

The odd thing was that I *did* know the difference between the two, but that wasn't as important to me as the memory Emma's bag had triggered. I wish I'd given myself the time to sort out my reactions before going with the shame option.

Stupid 2!

* * *

[Note from Jane: Ever since Sky's diagnosis, I've become more aware of people's casual use of the word "stupid" or "dumb" . . . and I'm learning to watch my language. We're so careful with our language so as to not offend various groups of traditionally marginalized people that I'm now finding "stupid" to mean more than I ever thought it did before. How about you?]

. . . .

JANE: WHAT IS MEMORY?

Sky has been reading several books about memory recently, and we've been talking about memory, what it is, and what it means. It turns out that there are many kinds of memory—ranging from memories of how to do things (ride a bike, use tools, walk) to memories of things that happened to us (however imperfect or incomplete those memories are) to memories of factual information (where is the bathroom? when did the Civil War begin?).

So I asked Sky, conversationally:

"What did we do yesterday?"

Pause.

"Ummmm."

Pause.

"We played disc golf."

"Yup. Where?"

Pause.

"Ummm, first we played in Waterbury. Then we played in Williston."

"What else?"

Pause.

"We got some food in between."

"Yup. And what did we do when we got home?"

Pause.

"Ummmmm."

Pause.

"We played Trains with Emma!"

"Right! And what did we do last weekend?"

"You expect me to remember that?!?!"

"Yes, I do. Think about it."

Pause.

Pause.

Pause.

"We didn't get to listen to *Wait, Wait, Don't Tell Me*."

"Yes. And why was that?"

"Ummmm, ummmm, ummmm, we were in Washington, DC, at the Climate March!"

"Nailed it."

Was it so important for Sky to remember these things? Was it necessary for me to ask him? We had a great time both days, doing fun and important things—isn't that what mattered most? Perhaps I should have asked him about the feelings that he'd had those days—would that have been easier to remember? Or maybe not ask him at all (really, it was just to test out these memory theories).

What memories are important for you to remember? How would it feel to not remember?

. . . .

SKY: STORE 1

Alzheimer's, you are so slow.
    I can run circles around you if I want to.
    To prove it, I just drew a clock . . .
    . . . took nineteen seconds . . .
    And it wasn't a bit difficult!!

    Unlike at the store yesterday: $6.41.
    First, I hand over a five and a one.
    I'd brought some change from home.
    So, I dump a few coins on the counter:
    Quarters, nickels, dimes, and two pennies.
    Uh-oh.

My mind gets seriously busy, jangling.
Way too many possibilities . . .
Most of them skyrocketing over $0.41.
Others not enough.
The store clerk is patient,
Watching me pushing the coins.
Around.
And around.

. . . .

SKY: STORE 2

The Vermont State Liquor Store is a busy place this Friday afternoon in May. The colleges are winding down, the students are winding up, and the one liquor store in town is shaking. Twenty-somethings dominate the store, both behind the counter and in the long, polite lines of customers waiting to check out. The store is prepared for the onslaught, with extra help at the checkouts.

There's one old guy, two or three times the age of everyone else. He's kind of disheveled, wearing work clothes. Despite his small purchase, he manages to hold up the line, emptying one of his pockets onto the counter.

Why?

Now the old guy is randomly sliding his pocketful of change across the counter at the clerk and muttering something.

Homeless, maybe?

Drunk, probably.

Or, he could've escaped from his nursing home . . .

Nope, just me in another cameo appearance as the Demented One!

. . . .

SKY: ALL ABOARD!

Sitting underground, in magnificently overstimulating New York City, waiting for an overnight train headed south.

But, first, word association time.

Railroad . . . Tobacco road . . . Dementia road . . . Road to nowhere? . . . Nowhere man? . . . No way, Jose!

Jane and I have the good fortune to have signed up for the North American conference of DAA, the Dementia Action Alliance. This is a group advocating for the continuing personhood of people living with dementia (what an idea!).

"Re-Imagine Life with Dementia" is the theme of the two-day conference, which starts tomorrow in Atlanta.

We expect to hear the perspectives of fellow people living creatively with Alzheimer's as care partners, those experiencing the condition directly, or community advocates. We do *not* expect to hear much of the words: "patient," "sufferer," or "victim."

Below are some random excerpts from the program descriptions of the workshops and plenary sessions:

Opening Session Keynote

Dementia is fast becoming recognized around the world as a disability condition necessitating attention to overall well-being. This keynote presented by an internationally recognized geriatrician, educator and specialist in caring for people with changing cognitive abilities will share insights into new global paradigms of living with dementia.

Positivity Is Life-Affirming

Through candid, heartwarming and funny stories, hear one individual's journey not to let Alzheimer's define him. Thinking, feeling, understanding and loving are still parts of everyday life as before—now with Alzheimer's added. Learn how positivity can make a significant difference in one's life from a cognitive psychology perspective.

Living Well with Dementia

Through video clips, personal experiences and audience interaction, discuss issues of stigmatization and the prevalence of a deficit-based approach to dementia care rather than a strengths-based approach. Explore ways to effect changes.

It's Not Time to Stop Living—Time to Connect and Live Fully!

Meaningfully supporting and participating in the lives of individuals with dementia takes care partners out of traditional roles. This interactive session explores balancing needs and wellbeing, rewards, risks and challenges, and provides useful strategies to stay connected and live fully.

I Am More Than My Diagnosis: Moving From Isolation to Inclusion

Led by the play performers living with dementia, audience members, working in small groups, will brainstorm and create prototype activities to support and encourage dialogue between individuals with dementia and those around them to bring back and share with their communities.

Remarkable Experiences: Music, Memory, and a Family's Creative Journey

Learn about the transformative responses triggered by meaningful music from the internationally recognized Music & Memory program, and a family's amazing experience using creative arts to support self-expression and joy for their loved one with dementia.

Transcending the Biomedical Status Quo to Support Living with Dementia

Members from the DAA's Scientific Advisory Board will engage the audience in candid discussions about the challenges and barriers created by traditional, biomedical practices faced by people and families living with dementia and ways to transcend the status quo.

Stay tuned for our report!
All aboard!!

JANE: FACE-TO-FACE WITH DEMENTIA

It is humbling and awe-inspiring to hang out with a bunch of people with dementia, and those who care about them. There's a quiet room here at the conference for people who need the space away from the hustle and bustle. I need it, and I don't even have dementia. I'm glad they welcome me.

Interesting conversations. People being real. Laughter. Questions. Sharing of ideas about support, welcoming, belonging.

Sky gets a care package given to those attending the conference who have dementia. A big selection of junk food. Some earplugs to cut down on noise ("Eargasm" earplugs). And the best—a double-sided sign that says "Please Speak Slower" on one side, and "It's Too Noisy" on the other, meant to hold up during keynote speeches and workshops . . . and maybe just regular life. I'll bet there are a lot of people who would appreciate such a sign.

Just a lot of caring people having hors d'oeuvres and drinking wine.

Can't wait for tomorrow.

. . . .

SKY: CONFERENCE

I'm finally sorting out my experience at the recent conference of the Dementia Action Alliance (DAA). Some may not agree that three weeks ago is still recent, but do not forget that this account is brought to you by someone who may be loosing the tethers of time. And if you are still bothered, well, take a chill pill, relax . . . it's summer!

The conference was held at a fancy, glass-enclosed hotel in Atlanta, Georgia. The place seemed well set up as a convention center, complete with a Grand Ballroom. Most amazing was the attendance: over 350 people, united by their acceptance and support of people living with dementia of all kinds. I hadn't expected to be so moved, but I was blown away by the diversity and intensity of the group.

Of course, there was humor: one of the plenary speakers described a family custom where his wife gives him a watch every year, even after his growing dementia made it impossible to read an analog clock. This explained his fashion statement of wearing fifteen-plus watches simultaneously during the gathering. Later he related an experience that had just occurred at the conference that morning. He was sitting in the plenary session when he felt his mind freeze, and turn off: "I was having a bad day, we all know what that is, right?" He stumbled awkwardly out of the ballroom in a fog. Somewhere else he might be assumed to be drunk or worse. As it turned out, an attendee noticed his troubles and cared for him. He got him up to his room on the twelfth floor and tucked him into bed, where he slept like a rock for two-plus hours and woke up with only a foggy memory of what had happened.

I was also the recipient of a straightforward act of kindness, on the elevator of all places. The hotel had made a few accommodations for the Onslaught of the Demented. For instance, a quiet room had been set aside at the end of an out-of-the-way corridor as a place to escape the energy that might accompany any crowd of 350 people. So, if you were stressed out you had a place to go . . . as long as you weren't too stressed out to find it!

But the architecture itself, while perhaps impressive for a business gathering, wasn't all that inspiring for our group, spatially challenged as many of us were. A few examples:

- The meeting rooms were mostly on the fourth floor.
- Except for a few that were on the first floor, which may or may not have been the lobby level.
- From which, open space towered (at strange angles) back up to the fourth floor.
- Escalators made their way up through this space as well, but they were turned off, perhaps as a safety measure. *[Jane's note: they had been turned off because many attendees with dementia found them too noisy and distracting.]*

And the elevators, oh, my. Just looking at them made me think longingly of the quiet room. The interior walls were a jagged and bizarre pastiche of life-size women happily working out, spotless mirrors, Trump-like gold everywhere, and some kind of highly textured floor covering, all on the walls. In your face!! Compared to all this manic busyness, the buttons for the floor numbers were so discreet as to be hard to find. For me, the elevators got more wild rather than less so over the two and a half days. One time I was in there, having pushed the button for Floor 4. People were coming and going. I pressed 4 again, and still nothing happened. A professional-looking lady stopped quickly and asked me if I wanted help. I thanked her and declined. She was fine about it, no obvious judgements, and the car emptied.

I pressed 4 again and you can guess what happened: Nothing. I was on Floor 4 the whole time!!

But I was safe . . . in the Community of the Demented.

SKY: NAVIGATING THE BIGGEST HOTEL IN THE WORLD

Do you think a person with a compromised sense of direction might have any issues getting around the biggest hotel in the world on his own?

OK, first of all, it's not the biggest in the world any more. It was the biggest, when it was built by the Pennsylvania Railroad in 1919 as the New York City flagship of the then mighty railroad. Today, the hotel still towers over Penn Station, and still dominates its hugely busy neighborhood. Due to its superb location and low-end room rates, Jane and I stayed there on the way to the conference in Atlanta.

The place is a throwback to the glory days of rail travel, when trains were literally the only way to go. The lobby is still crowded with international travelers, and it takes only a bit of imagination to picture nattily dressed sophisticates crossing the lobby to dine at the Statler Grill or dance at the Café Rouge ballroom while listening to the Glenn Miller Orchestra, Count Basie, or the Dorsey Brothers. Today, most of the 1,700 rooms are tiny by modern standards, perhaps contributing to the hotel's decision to reduce rates instead of upgrading the rooms' footprints. Two elegant remaining touches are:

- High (nine-foot-plus) ceilings, a practical way to keep the rooms comfortable before air conditioning.
- Massive stone walls on the exterior, providing the same function.

Though the hotel's statistics now rank it as fourth largest in the city, 1,700 rooms under one roof remains pretty impressive. The hotel's architects chose to go with a grid design, efficiently packing the rooms into *long* rows that intersect at right angles. Some, but not all, of these seemingly endless corridors intersect with other rows, always at ninety degrees. Standing at an intersection, I could look into the distance and see the vanishing point, where parallel lines meet in a single spot. Discovering this phenomenon inspired both awe and anxiety. Vertigo knocked rudely on my brain. I experimented with walking to the next intersection, and as I had dreaded, it looked exactly like the previous one and had three options for corridors reaching deeper inside. Anxiety was not letting up. Ruder than ever. I reached for my phone for comfort. Yes, it was still there. And yes, I still had service. So yes, Jane could come and rewind the invisible thread connecting me to a world that made sense.

This time I made it back without help (only two or three wrong turns . . . I think). I suspect that the confidence I felt knowing that my safety net was in place helped me be a bit smarter negotiating the Hotel Pennsylvania fun house.

An adventure every minute.

All at no extra charge!

. . . .

SKY: TAKING THE TEST 2

If you want to rent a sailboat at the Community Sailing Center in Burlington, you have to pass a test. A couple of days ago I visited this place just to look around, and I wound up sitting on a box, pencil in hand, about to face down a written test. Now, for someone on the dementia continuum, the idea of a cognitive test of any kind is likely to be anxiety-producing. And, of course, experiencing anxiety, no matter what the source, is virtually guaranteed to lead to more anxiety, which then leads to more of the same, with a resulting weakened cognitive function. Somehow, the conversation had got a little ahead of me, and that must have been when I agreed to give the Test a shot. Luckily, I didn't yet know the protocol where you are only allowed to take the test once, and if you fail, you have to take some kind of a remedial course.

Countering my stress was a certain confidence in my sailing experience. I had just calculated that I had first "sailed"—i.e., ridden in a small sailboat—exactly sixty years ago, and learned to sail on my own a year or two later. Since then I think I have sailed more summers than I haven't. Mostly, I was going by the theory that, like riding a bike, once you know how to do it, you just don't forget.

Countering my confidence was the stress of the past few years of unpredictably forgetting all kinds of things. The concept of "things you just don't forget" now seems more quaint than unassailable.

So, would this written test be smart enough to tap into my nautical reserves that I was counting on "just not forgetting"?

Would I be smart enough to pull up words and concepts across decades of time?

Short answer: yes and yes!

Multiple choice would have been easier, but I was able to write down names of various parts of the boat, like the sheet—not rope—that goes to the boom. I guessed (correctly) which was the starboard tack, and I knew that the boat on this tack has the right-of-way.

I pulled up three reasonable ways to tell which way the wind was blowing.

On a roll, I identified *reach, beating, halyard, beam reach*, and more.

The staff person graded the test with me, a prospect I found mildly terrifying since I thought I had relied on a fair amount of guesswork. But my "guesses" turned out to be mostly right on.

I passed, and it was a good day!

And now, a final question from the test:

True or false: A sailboat has the right-of-way over the ferry.

Hint: Stay away from ferries.

ALZHEIMER'S CANYON
Episode 3

[In case you don't remember(!!!), we last left our intrepid traveler, the one on the one-way detour, at the Alzheimer's Café . . .]

It turns out that my meal is just what the doctor ordered, nutritious, tasty, and not too filling. Maybe it's the triple shot of turmeric, but I feel like moving around, doing something besides sitting around digesting.

Not that those marathoners are any inspiration. They seem to have taken to aiding their digestion with random calisthenics, punctuated with grunts and smiles. My guess is that they're so smug because, unlike mere mortals, they say they are not living under a death sentence. They've figured out how to beat the system. As their mentor, Jack LaLanne, crowed, "Death would be bad for my image." Then, as quickly as they arrived at the café, they are out the door, flexing, preening, and grinning as they go.

"Wow," I say to the maître d'. "What's the story with those guys?"

"Oh, yeah. They're special. At least *they* think so. Rim Runners," he snorts.

"Rim Runners?"

"Yes, Rim Runners, sir. Cocky bastards, I call 'em. They think their latest diet fad will save their sorry, bulked-up asses. So they spend their time running around here on the rim, congratulating themselves on how smart they are. Funny thing . . . they don't look all that smart when they get blown off the edge."

"Blown off the edge? I never heard of that," I tell him.

"Of course you haven't. But I see it every day, from the restaurant. You might not believe all the people who have gone down, and the ways they've gone down. It's mostly on the quiet, you know what I mean? The Rim Runners sure aren't going to brag about it."

"What about you? You seem pretty blasé about this whole thing. I mean, here's a Canyon that's not on any map, and it sucks people up without warning and . . ."

"Well, it's not that bad a job, really. My daughters and I are pretty well used to it by now. Somebody's gotta keep up the basics."

"Oh, gee, that was your daughter working at the Welcome Center? I'm afraid I might not have been that polite to her."

"It happens a lot, what with the detour and all." The oily smile was creeping over his face again.

"OK, my man, I think it's time for me to take a wander . . ." Did I really say that? Take a wander?

Checking my pockets, I realize I can't cover the fancy dinner I just ate. God, this place is weird!

Maître d' has seen all this before. "You're in the system, right?" he asks.

I nod.

"Then we'll take it from here. Have you changed your address yet?"

"Wait! What? Why would I ne-n- . . . ?"

"Oh, just keeping the billing up-to-date, sir." The oil's getting thicker now, and I'm imagining a full-blown anxiety event coming on. Definitely time to hit the road. There's just one problem: no more car.

Uh-oh . . . two problems: no more road.

Mister maître d', always helpful, offers, "You've got your guide. Remember?"

"You didn't give me any guide!"

"You have what you need. Remember?"

"Remember! Remember! What am I supposed to remember? You never told me I had to Remember! YOU NEVER TOLD ME I HAD TO REMEMBER!" I'm pacing now. Pacing and shouting at the smarmy waiter. Has he really told me something important?

(Silence.)

I JUST DON'T REMEMBER!!

MOVING ON AND REACHING OUT: OUR YEAR OF PUBLIC SERVICE

One year out, Sky continued to want to find his people and to be public about his dementia. The DAA conference, the radio show, and the blog energized him, and he suggested we put together a sermon and a workshop and offer it to Unitarian Universalist (UU) congregations around New England. Our first presentation went well, so I contacted my colleagues and offered our services. We soon had twenty-five engagements scheduled over the year, from Maine to Washington state, in both UU as well as United Church of Christ congregations. We were well-received everywhere, and Sky took pleasure in meeting other people with dementia. He even handled the travel fairly well—mostly.

Along with the sermon/workshop project, we also spoke to several classes at the local university, and participated in a panel discussion about dementia. Sky was honored to be chosen as the "face of dementia" for the annual Alzheimer's walk. Our blog readership grew. Sky continued his volunteer work in the community.

And, not finding a support group that worked for us, we started one of our own for people with dementia and their loved ones. We met monthly to talk—loved ones in one group, people with dementia in another group—but Sky was disappointed as none of the people with dementia wanted to talk about it. In fact, most of them denied that anything was wrong, and they wondered why their loved ones had dragged them to this meeting. After four months, we called it quits.

In the meantime, we learned that we would be receiving an inheritance from Sky's aunt. Mary Ellen was a single woman and had left her estate to her nieces and nephew: Sky and his sisters. I wanted to immediately put the money into the "Sky care" account, but Sayer, Emma, and Dana suggested that we should have a family camp on a lake. They argued that all of our houses were too small for the whole family, and that a larger space where we could be together was important at this point. Besides, we all loved being on the water—Sky especially. I set about looking at properties around northern Vermont and in the Adirondacks.

A friend of a friend approached me about buying our house in New Orleans. As much as I hated to, I knew it was the right thing to do. Then a friend of a friend approached me about buying *Antinous*. This was a bigger struggle, and Sky wanted nothing to do with it. As unhappy as I was about this, I also knew it was the right thing to do. The last house, and the last boat, down. With both relief and sadness, we were finally free of outside obligations.

September came, and Emma left us to spend a year in England getting her master's degree at Cambridge. We were all very sad to see her go but knew this was important for her. Thanks to modern technology, Emma often participated in our game nights via FaceTime. It was almost like she was still at home.

Unfortunately, our cat, Leo, disappeared around the time Emma left, and Sky was beside himself with worry.

A month of advertising, searching, and hoping for Leo's safe return to no avail, I decided to go to the animal shelter and adopt another cat. Tubby promptly disappeared, and Sky, once again, was beside himself with worry and spent every day walking the neighborhood looking for him. Five days later, Tubby returned, very hungry and a bit forlorn. Sky was ecstatic. Thankfully, Tubby never left us again and would spend hours sitting on Sky's lap.

That fall, Sky was thrilled to get the family piano back. Because of our itinerant life, the piano had been living with Dana, but it couldn't be moved into her second-floor condo because of a narrow, tight hallway. Now that we were staying put, and lived on the first floor, the piano became ours again. While he was too embarrassed to play in front of others, in the pre-dementia days Sky had loved to spend time at the keyboard playing James Taylor, Bob Dylan, Beatles, and Broadway songs. I loved listening to him, and was so happy he had the opportunity to play again. But the thrill was short lived. Sky complained that when he looked at the keyboard, he saw 176 keys instead of 88, and not only that, they were constantly moving. We made an appointment with a neuro-ophthalmologist so Sky could be tested. The result: nothing organically wrong, it was just his dementia. He tried periodically over the next few months to play, to no avail. The piano stayed silent.

In October, we headed out on a trip of a different kind. One of my colleagues was offering "life review" services. This entailed meeting with her for a couple of hours every morning and afternoon for three days while you told her about your life, its high and low points; she asked good questions; and you left with some kind of focus of what to aim for next. It was a retreat of sorts, where you stayed in her guest house, she fed you three meals a day of your choosing, and you had peace and quiet to think about things, and to be together without obligations. She had never worked with a couple before but was intrigued, so Sky and I headed for Minnesota to meet with her. It was everything we could have hoped for. We felt nourished, listened to, optimistic about our year of public service ahead, and making the most of our dementia journey together. Sky even handled the travel well.

However well Sky handled travel, he did not handle returning home very well. His anxiety continually increased, and his short-term memory decreased. He would become temporarily lost, incontinent, and unable to motivate himself to do anything. Transitions became hard for him. He would complain, "If this is 'early' and this is 'easy,' I'm not looking forward to things getting worse." Luckily, I was still able to leave Sky for short periods of time—a weekend, or a couple of days away—as long as Sayer checked in on him, making sure he was eating and feeding the cats. I enjoyed the respite, and it gave me a chance to gather my strength to return home to this new person who was paranoid, anxious, and fussing, fussing, fussing all the time. I was grateful for the sermon and workshop engagements: "I'm not glad he has dementia, but at least it gives me something to do." I began to wonder what life would be like when he was gone.

I had no luck finding a lakeside cottage that slept six, but I did find a beautiful piece of property for a reasonable price an hour from our home—and I bought it. Dana, Sayer, and Emma set about designing the perfect camp, complete with full first-floor accessibility for if and when Sky would need that. I secured the necessary engineer, excavator, electrician, plumber, and foundation people. It was time to build another house! I was excited—I love housebuilding—but Sky was not. He was scared to death of everything that might go wrong, including his inability to participate. With assurances from Dana and Sayer (and Emma on her return) that they would help as they could, along with a friend who was a professional carpenter, I promised Sky we could do it.

The morning we were laying the insulation for the foundation, I began having chest pain. I stopped work and tried to rest, but the spasm-like pain increased until it was strong enough that I had to breathe through each spasm like childbirth contractions. Sky had grown uncomfortable with driving, but there was no way I could—and I knew I needed to go to the hospital. Could I be having a heart attack?

I spent thirty hours in the hospital being tested for every cardiac anything. All tests negative—my heart was in perfect condition. That was a relief, but what was this pain? It had taken eight milligrams of morphine to even start to soothe it. The doctors wondered if it was pancreatitis, so I was tested for that. Nope. Perhaps an ulcer? Also nope. With the pain gone, and no diagnosis, I was sent home. The whole family was freaked out, none more so than Sky. Who would take care of him if something was wrong with me? I had no further trouble, however. Six months later, a gastroenterologist would tell me that I had possibly suffered an esophageal spasm, which can happen for no reason at all.

I was fine, it was summer, and it was time to start building. Sky reluctantly accompanied me to the building site, where I put together the walls. Sky acted as my gofer, schlepping two-by-fours and being my muscle when it was time to lift the walls into place. But he didn't like it—the noise, the chaos, the fear someone would get hurt, the frustration that he couldn't do any carpentry work at all. We stuck with it anyway, and the house slowly took shape. We brought up our kayaks, and I bought a Sunfish so Sky could go sailing. We were on a lake, after all. It was time to have fun!

SKY: WHY AM I DOING THIS?

Why am I doing this?

People who know me know that, by and large, I'm not one to spend a lot of time blowing my own horn. Why should anyone care if I'm having a hard time figuring out a tip or who might be holding the queen of hearts?

I'm pleasantly surprised that writing and reflecting on my experience helps me to feel more confident and less overwhelmed. Like for the traveler who finds himself on the detour to Alzheimer's Canyon with a map of blank pages, a little guidance goes a long way.

So one reason to write is self-serving: it helps me to understand and learn from the often confusing new life I've got going on.

And, if other people on the Alzheimer's detour, or with friends and loved ones on the detour, feel some comfort or support from these words, all the better! We demented ones and our care partners need to be recognized, respected, and above all, listened to as we stumble along this journey we never asked to take.

I'm living with the assumption that understanding and compassion are essential to this world we all share. My plan is to go on chronicling my experiences just as long as I remain able to do so.

Hang on tight!

SKY: ONE YEAR IN

A few weeks ago a day quietly went by that marked my first full year with my "probable early stage Alzheimer's" diagnosis. Like most of what is "known" about Alzheimer's and its progression, this anniversary itself was as quiet as it was relentless. Maybe this would be a good time for a review, a kind self-assessment?

Or maybe not . . .

Instead, how about a few random observations?

According to researchers, the attack on my brain has probably been in progress for some years, only surfacing now for unknown reasons.

It's not an anniversary I want to celebrate, really, but it inevitably gets me wondering about who and how I'll be at anniversaries to come. So far, I feel like I've kept myself ahead of the curve in some ways. I've been able to feel superior to those Alzheimer critters trying to sabotage my brain. I've been known to mock the lethargy and unreliable pace of those unseen varmints doing their unwelcome things up there. Sometimes, it's personal.

Despite noticeable cognitive declines and memory holes, I aced my neurological assessment last spring, showing no decline since the previous one. Hah!!

I can usually fake it as necessary:

"Really, you don't look like you have it. Are you kidding me?"

"I wish."

JANE: LOSSES, GREAT AND SMALL

Six years ago, I accidentally amputated the end of my left thumb. Due to circumstances, I was over an hour from a hospital, and during my journey there, I wondered if they would be able to reattach it or not. What if I lost the last inch of my thumb? I finally decided that it would be OK—I would adapt.

Fortunately, the repair was a success. But, while it was healing, there were some things I couldn't do—the biggest being able to knit. I am an avid knitter, and it was really bugging me to not be able to do that. I eventually managed to, slowly, with the big bandage on my left hand. Once the bandage got smaller, my physical therapist encouraged me to knit even more, saying it would help me get the movement back in my thumb.

Loss regained.

Eleven years ago, our daughter broke both wrists and detached a tendon in her left elbow in an accident. For two weeks, due to her bulky casts, she was unable to do anything—from scratching her nose to turning the pages of a book to feeding herself or getting dressed. She went from a competent, able young adult to a helpless infant—except that she, at least, could tell us what she wanted!

After two weeks, she had the use of one hand, and she learned how to dress herself, feed herself, and do any number of things that she hadn't been able to do just a week before. After six weeks, she was pretty much back to where she had been before the accident.

These were small losses, even though they felt pretty big at the time. We all face losses, of all kinds—great and small.

A relationship doesn't work out. Our loved ones die. In a moment, you can go from being fully able to being disabled. Over a creeping period of time, you can go from being fully able to being permanently disabled. We never know, and we may not be able to control the outcome.

Either way, it sucks. We want to trust our bodies, trust our minds. We want to keep going with the plans we had, with the life we had envisioned.

How does that old saying go? Life is what happens when you're busy making other plans . . .

I am feeling loss pretty deeply these days. It's been a challenging year since Sky's diagnosis, and we've done a lot— renovated a new home, traveled, found new volunteer work, reconnected with old friends, created this blog, and had lots of fun. And lots of tears.

But. I'm done with this now. Time for something new— or old. I'd kinda like to go back to my old life, pre-diagnosis. I want the old Sky back. I want the old me back.

Unfortunately, there is no going back. I can cry and fume and fuss, but our old life is not coming back. There is deep grief with this enormous loss. Yes, we're moving forward on this new path, trying to create something positive and empowering. And, at the same time, we have absolutely no idea the trajectory of this disease for Sky—how long it will take for him to lose different abilities, and which ones, and in what order. We have absolutely no idea what it will be like for me, how I will handle things, how it will affect me physically and spiritually, or how it will affect our kids.

Lest any of you are worried about us, we are doing all we can to deal with this—eating well, exercising, talking with professionals and friends about our fear of the unknown and our sense of loss, having fun, and doing what we can while we can. Appreciating every moment.

But, for me right now, this sense of loss hangs over me like a black cloud. Perhaps there will be a wonderful thunderstorm to wash it all away (but, please, no hurricanes!).

. . . .

SKY: GLEN CAMPBELL

Glen Campbell died last week. He lived a public struggle to continue his musical career in the face of Alzheimer's. He and his musical family arranged a five-week farewell tour after his diagnosis that quickly grew into a fifteen-week extravaganza of over 150 concerts.

A documentary film crew follows along on the tour, recording the ups and downs of the shows as well as the Campbells' home life. As the tour becomes more and more intense, the film crew becomes more and more a part of the odyssey. Several family members are also part of the backup band, and as Campbell's condition grows more severe, there are some tense moments as the show must go on, even if the star of the show doesn't know where he is.

Overall, the feeling is one of a family rising to the occasion with love, support, and musical talent. Tens of thousands of fans, all aware of Campbell's condition, cheer him and his family on, night after night after night. He even cowrote for the movie, one of the most chilling songs I have ever heard about dementia, "I'm Not Gonna Miss You."

The movie is called *Glen Campbell: I'll Be Me*. It is available on YouTube. It's great at showing the ups and downs of deciding to be out about the diagnosis.

. . . .

SKY: WHO ARE THE EXPERTS?

Who are the experts around here?
   Who knows what's going on?
   What's next? When?
   How much time do we have?
   Where do we look for help?
   A year ago, after enough people told me to get my head examined, I got my head examined . . . and my world changed forever. A whirlwind of practitioners had their way with me to see if any of their specialized knowledge could shed light on what was going on inside my ragged little brain.
   Technicians took away buckets of blood to test for a humongous list of maladies. (Now I know for sure I don't have syphilis. I guess I can be relieved about that!) I was interviewed by a psychologist and took a battery of psychometric exams to check out my cognitive capabilities.
   Twice, I was slid into a space-age machine. Once to perform an MRI scan of my brain at rest and look for tumors or other bad stuff. The second time to check what happened as my brain was fed a special treat of IV glucose seasoned with radioactive isotopes to compare how efficiently various parts were doing their jobs.
   The person in charge of all this was the director of the memory center, Dr. P., a veteran neurologist who has been

diagnosing people with Alzheimer's and other dementias for over twenty years. He was quiet, steady, and calm, with an excellent bedside manner. Jane and I met with him several times as we negotiated the complexities of arriving at and talking about a diagnosis. We quickly built a rapport, and I trusted his expertise. In those early days, I needed a rock, and he took on that role for me.

But, as time passed, I started to notice what the musician David Byrne calls "sand in the Vaseline." Part of it was my own fault. I wanted to know *everything* about the fearsome world I was due to enter, and the memory center didn't have answers. I was heartened and consoled by their offer to monitor me periodically over the years ahead (oh, I have years?) and generally keep an eye on things. Dr. P. suggested that we get our legal affairs in order as soon as possible and prepare ourselves financially, whatever that meant. I said I'd like to join a support group, and Jane asked what resources were available for her. Dr. P. said he had no idea and referred us to the social worker associated with the center.

The salve gets grittier . . .

We dutifully make an appointment with the social worker and find out that Dr. P. was correct in knowing nothing about services for families because there aren't any. The social worker told us that her caseload included so many hundreds of families that she was impossibly overloaded, as her position was only half time. There was a chance that a grant might come through to allow her to do more, but we shouldn't count on it.

Dr. P. was good about answering questions, and I was good at asking. (The reverse, not so much. Dr. P. had surprisingly few questions for me. Or maybe I was just too busy asking my own.) The combination was a recipe for at least a halfway productive conversation, and we had a few good ones. Problems came as I pressed for details about what to expect. I wanted to know what happens next and what happens after that. I became upset as Dr. P., with his twenty-plus years in neurology, seemed to give me just platitudes:

- Everyone's path is different.
- There is really no way to predict . . .
- You could live twenty years, or . . .
- The course of the disease varies in a major way from person to person.
- We will keep an eye out and adjust treatments as necessary.
- Drugs can help some people with some symptoms, sometimes.
- I can't really predict how long you will be able to read or carry on a conversation.

And my two favorites:

- Everyone agrees that exercise is good.
- [Uh-oh . . .]

My irritation softened as I learned—mostly through independent reading and talking with people with dementia—that, sure enough, the "platitudes," while annoying, were also largely true! Dr. P. was not just dangling me along. There really is an unpredictable variety of courses for the condition. The medical knowledge base about dementia, the things scientists know for sure, while increasing by itty bits, is remarkably thin.

(Closely related is the unimpressive array of drugs for "treatment." As I mention elsewhere, the drugs, if they do anything at all, serve only to temporarily alleviate some symptoms, not to reverse or even to slow the course of the disease. Drug use can be an effort to prepare the ground to make the body a less hospitable place for the plaques and tangles of dementia—e.g., Lipitor and other statins to modify cholesterol. Drugs are also used to try to counteract the side effects of other drugs. But don't get me started on drugs . . . !)

I want to finish this by reflecting on dementia and wisdom. I am coming to believe that dementia may possibly be found sometimes skulking around wisdom's back door. It is possible for dementia to make people smart!

"Yeah, right," you say. "Dementia is the *opposite* of smart! What, are you crazy?! Got a few screws loose? Not playing with a full deck? Cuck-oo? Cuck-oo? Cuck-oo?"

OK, here's just a few ways that demented people can be smart:

- We often can slow down and experience "reality" at a different pace.
- We can often be comfortable with more silence in conversations, both internal and with others, resulting in an appreciation of quietness in self and others.
- We can often literally see things others miss. When I pay attention, it's easy to see patterns in trees and rocks for instance. Pleasant, no-cost, no-risk, no-drug "highs."
- Through experience, we can learn ways to work with anxiety and fears when they arise.

- We have the opportunity to provide effective self-care, based on our intimate knowledge of our changing selves and interaction with other self-aware people living with the condition.

Of course, all of these and other positive sides of dementia have their dark and frightening counterparts. More than we welcome. More than we can stand, sometimes.

Nevertheless, we all must continue to appreciate and protect the precious baby in the grungy bathwater.

SKY: THE ELEPHANT IN THE ROOM

I want to introduce you to my new friend.

Her name is Mnemo (NEE-mo), and she has a memory you wouldn't believe! Her brain has three times the neurons of mere humans. A lot of that "extra" brainpower goes to making her huge body so graceful and athletic, leaving her a kajillion of billions of neurons to power her phenomenal memory. In many areas, her short-term and long-term memory each outshine humans', demented or not. Mnemo doesn't waste her neurons memorizing numbers or lists or appointments, but she will *never* forget a face. Cool, huh?

Mnemo and I go a lot of places together. We are allies. She especially likes social situations, more than I do. And she can keep me on track. Kind of like playing with dolls, maybe, Mnemo lets me dress her up. Well, we call it dress-up. It didn't take us long to realize that if you want to do anything at all in life besides dressing up an elephant, don't dress up that elephant.

We settled on me outfitting Mnemo with attractive and interesting signs, one on each massive side. Currently, her signs read: no cure and onward.

Here's a fun thing we did last month . . .

A friend of a friend approaches me and lets me know that he's heard about my Alzheimer's. He tells me about his friend with dementia, how everybody rallied around him and created a program for him that was to cure his disease. Mnemo was biding her time, listening, eyes and ears wide open.

Glancing at Mnemo, I remind the stranger, "Alzheimer's is a terminal illness. No one recovers."

"Yeah, but no, we had a whole team. We had a program. You have to do every step. It's amazing!"

I can't tell if the stranger can see Mnemo, but I can. Did she just wink one of her dinner plate eyes at me? Turning back to the stranger I say, "You know, I've come this far, and I've got an idea of how far I've still got to go. I need to put my energy into making my time left just as meaningful as it can be. I've got to stay grounded and not get diverted by pie-in-the-sky ideas, delicious as they may seem. But, thanks, man, really, I do appreciate your concern. So many people just shut down and run away when they glimpse this beautiful elephant in the room. Have a good evening."

"And you, Sky. Have a good life!"

"What's left of it!" I grin.

I start to walk away, but turn back. "Oh . . . and your friend?"

"He died."

ALZHEIMER'S CANYON
Episode #4

[For those who may not remember, we last left our detoured adventurer outside the Alzheimer's Café. He'd had a day that had more than pushed his personal boundaries of sanity, and was in the middle of a disturbing meltdown.

Wait! What?

Yes, he feels he is becoming more knowledgeable than he wants to be about living in a world that is far from what it seems. Little does he suspect how much more learning is ahead . . .]

Ugh!! Rough landing! Sand everywhere.

Nothing feels broken though. Can wiggle everything, all right?

Ooh, my head. I'm gonna get an egg there for sure. Tender.

Wow, get a grip now, pal. Let's figure this out. Where am I? And how do I get outta here?

I'm clinging to a narrow finger of sandy rock. Every time I move I scrape off more grains of sand, which silently disappear below. Everywhere I can see from here looks the same. OMG, I'm in Alzheimer's Canyon!!

And look, there's Monsieur Maître d'Oily, way up there on that ridge.

"Hey, monsieur! It's me. Down here! Got a rope?" I shout at him, waving my arms.

He's just standing there.

"Hey, what about dessert? How is the turmeric/kale vegan tiramisu today? Ha ha, just kidding . . ." I have to scream at him, and still he pays no attention.

"No, really, I think I'm gonna need a hand getting back up there. This sand is as slippery as anything!

"I really don't have a handhold, or a foothold either," I add.

Why doesn't he say anything? Instead, he just points to a spot on the canyon wall to my left. Then, still without a word, he disappears over the rim.

Now that I am completely alone, I notice that my palms and the soles of my feet are sweating as I contemplate my slim collection of options:

I have to go somewhere, sometime soon. I will need food and water to survive, if I don't slip off this mountain first.

Going up doesn't seem promising. I swear that jerk of a maître d' heard every word I said before he turned his back on me and left. And besides, the evidence grows every minute that this guy could be a no-holds-barred psychopath or sadist or whatever.

It's just too steep and slippery to think about going up or down.

That leaves sideways, and the maître d's mystery spot.

It doesn't take long to figure out that traversing is the least suicidal of all the choices. And who knows? I might even make it to the monsieur's spot! At least I'll have a destination.

* * *

Meanwhile, the sun has slipped beyond the horizon, leaving the bulk of the Canyon in complete darkness. But the full moon shines strong in the bowl I'm clinging to, reflected around by the sandy cliffs. I can't really worry if I can make it across. I just have to.

I have to make a conscious effort to keep my toes from randomly curling up, but I keep going.

I never knew my hands could sweat this much, but I keep going.

Keep going . . .

Then, suddenly, as I squeeze around a corner, there's the spot. Though it's only twenty feet or so away, it still resembles nothing else but . . . a spot, something made by humans. Scrambling closer, it's obvious that the dark spot is nothing other than the end of a very big metal pipe angling upwards into the slick rock.

There's even a company name stamped on it: San-Di-Flush.

I find a curious little shelf below the pipe outlet, where I can rest in somewhat less hair-raising conditions, and I try to do just that, and stretch out on the shelf. Smooth. Nice.

I've got to think, to puzzle this out. My head is hurting trying to imagine what is going on here when I realize it's not just my overloaded brain, but I'm listening to actual *noises* coming down the (unclimbable) pipe. Industrial noises.

Wait! What?

Will the game ever stop changing down here? And will I always be so alone? Perched on the edge of a monstrous, death-dealing wilderness, and no one—*no one*—around.

Sand starts dribbling out of the pipe overhead, I feel a groaning sound, and all at once I know for sure that I'm not safe here on my polished shelf.

Everything is wrong, and unless I want to die in this forsaken place, I've got to go.

NOW!!

SKY: GAME NIGHT

I grew up in a family that appreciated games. The game closet was always overflowing, and playing games was the go-to activity if the weather was bad or we just didn't know what else to do.

My parents were avid bridge players for years before their own neurological issues and frustrations took their toll. I remember (yes, I do remember!) Bridge Nights, when my parents moved all the downstairs furniture around and dragged out the card tables for the massive evenings of duplicate bridge. I also remember feeling too young to understand the complicated system whereby each table played the same hands and somehow kept score on special pre-printed score sheets.

I also remember that it was fine not to know how they did it. It was a different world than mine. The tables were head-high. Special adult beverages appeared, and it was no place for little Sky to pad around in his fuzzy jammies with the plastic feet, cute as I might have been! I trudge upstairs to see what my sisters are up to.

> *The Game of Life, Chutes and Ladders, Sorry, or Clue.*
> *Or just shuffle some cards, if nothing else to do.*
> *Rummy 500 or Gin.*
> *No need to keep score just as long as I win.*

* * *

Flash forward sixty years to another game table, this one holding four adults, my family. The game tonight is Hogwarts Battle. The pace is rollicking, the players loud and laughing. An elephant snores in a corner.

We are playing a cooperative game where all the players work together to keep the evil Lord Voldemort and his hench-persons from dominating the world. The skill is in cleverly building resources that then interact with resources shared by others on your team of the good guys. In other words, planning ahead, preparing for and prevailing in conflict situations, and making quick complex decisions. It's also helpful to remember the attributes of various characters and how they change in the presence of other characters. Finally, each person must remain in communication with all the others, creating and maintaining a long-term strategy to identify and keep pressure on the few weaknesses of He-Who-Must-Not-Be-Named while at the same time protecting yourself and your team.

If you guessed that these are not skills particularly strong in someone on the dementia continuum, you would be right. You may also wonder why I might choose to subject myself to what could be a cognitive train wreck and call it fun.

1. My family members, game-players all, have been encouraging me.
2. Once I read on the box that the game was recommended for players ages eleven and up, my personal pride came into play.
3. With three younger sisters, two children of my own, and all their friends over the years, I'd played enough Candy Land (ages three and up) for a lifetime. Maybe I could hold the line at age eleven for a while.
4. A powerful reason to give the game the old college try was Mnemo, now sound asleep and snoring gently. I am happy to see my friend so relaxed and calm, because my friend's life isn't always that way. People, all

kinds of different kinds of people, tend to get cranky in her presence. They say mean things. Or they may ignore her completely. Her tough hide and massive brain serve her well.

My family gets it. They get Mnemo. They accept her and welcome her. And then I can relax, too, and feel stronger.

No cure, onward.

I try the game. It's complicated. My learning curve is steep, but with my teammates' patience and sense of fun, it's manageable. The pace of the game is a little slower with me, but no one seems to be counting.

We have a great time!

Thanks, Mnemo.

A note on no. 2 and no. 3 above: Although the thought processes outlined here did help motivate me to attempt something difficult, they border on dangerous territory. If I decide that my self-image, who I am, is tied to an arbitrary number, in this case eleven, then I set myself up for humiliation, despair, or worse if I don't measure up.

"Beating the numbers" is not a winning strategy for dementia.

Listen to Mnemo:

No cure.

Onward.

SKY: GOOD COACH

A lot has been written lately about ways to "prevent" or "delay" dementia.

Twenty-four researchers in a study recently published in the *Lancet* reviewed the literature and found that the following factors impact dementia risk:

- Avoiding or treating hearing loss in mid-life.
- Avoiding diabetes and obesity.
- Getting an education (remaining in school after the age of fifteen).
- Getting physical exercise.
- Not smoking.
- Reducing depression and social isolation.
- Reducing high blood pressure.[6]

I was surprised to see that keeping the brain busy did not make the list. I thought "use it or lose it" was common knowledge when it comes to physical and mental fitness as we age. Dr. P. puts physical exercise at the top of the list, and I tend to agree with him. I notice how quickly I tend to lose bodily fitness when I'm not keeping active. Why should brain fitness be any different? So I will just (very unscientifically) fold brain fitness into the physical exercise category, above.

For my physical self, I do yoga, eat well, and try to ride my bike a lot.

The brain fitness program is where the fun comes in. My son, Sayer, showed up a while ago with *The Mammoth*

---

6. Gill Livingston et al., "Dementia Prevention, Intervention, and Care," Lancet, 2017; 390: 2673-2734.

Book of Brain Boosters: Give your brain the ultimate work-out every day of the year! Inside are hundreds of puzzles. Math puzzles. Logic puzzles. Language puzzles. Visual puzzles. Spatial puzzles.

(Too many of them resemble the tests at the neurologist's office, where the problems get harder and harder and harder until you die.)

It's a subtle business, trying to keep my brain as exercised as possible without burning out.

And let me tell you, a burned-out brain on the dementia continuum is not a pretty sight! The key is a coach who can see the big picture and the small picture at the same time. Someone who can set out challenging rules and then enforce them as needed. Someone who can appreciate a difficult problem and give appropriate support. Someone being patient and encouraging and steady. And someone who can keep on having a *good time.*

I've got them all in my coach.

Thanks, Sayer!

. . . .

SKY: ALZHEIMER'S SLEAZE

Today I pulled up a video on the computer that promised a cure for Alzheimer's. Yep, a reversal of symptoms in twenty-one days. Complete cure in a month. All with ingredients from your local grocery store. This, after a dramatic prediction from the video's would-be "neurologist" that, without the treatment plan they offer, the person with Alzheimer's whom they profile in the video would be unable to recognize her own children after three months. After all, her MRI scan showed her brain to be mostly transformed into "a big black hole."

The narrator of the video urged viewers to act fast because at any minute the website might be taken down by the powers-that-be at the multinational Big Pharma legal drug cartels.

As someone on the dementia continuum, I found the video more than a little creepy. It was narrated by a handsome, earnest-looking guy who described himself as a science teacher from Stamford, Connecticut. His wife, the person with Alzheimer's (now totally cured!), was supposedly an English teacher in the same wealthy community.

Their sales pitch was disturbing on a number of levels. I saw more of it than I wanted to because the video was put up without the usual controls to pause or stop it. Weird.

Weirder still was the message of the unfairness to these nice, smart, well-off people of being cheated out of the life they are entitled to, ripped off by big, nasty corporations.

I'd tell you the magic potion of common secret ingredients if I'd made it to the end, but I fear I'd have needed to turn over a credit card to become an insider, don't you think?

There is only so much of that fear-mongering and magic-for-sale that I can take.

People living with dementia have more than enough pain to deal with without these parasites trying to make money off of it.

I know I do!

SKY: FINDING A SPOT

Right now I'm reading yet another book from the library about dementia. By now, I've at least glanced at each book in their collection, and read a number of them from cover to cover with care and interest. What's different for me about this one is that it's targeted to caregivers. So far I've been avoiding these books, fussing that they ignore the unique experience and needs of those of us living with the brain assault directly. Instead, they can get caught up in the details of coping with all the problems the affected person brings along to the family members caring for them.

Until this book came along, it's been easy to whine a variation of, "I know that most caregivers have thankless jobs and need all the support they can find, but . . ." or, crankier, "Hey, I'm the one with the incurable, fatal disease, here; how come I have to search so hard for a little support?"

Anyway, back to my reading. First, the title had caught my eye: *When Your Loved One Has Dementia: A Simple Guide for Caregivers*. A slim, unpretentious little volume, the authors' credit is shared by five women. The tone is down-to-Earth and respectful, without sugar-coating a thing. For instance, right in the middle of the section on communicating with your demented partner, they drop in this cruel little nugget, words that eloquently summarize the despair that devastates both partners:

"One of the difficult things about dementia for you is losing the support and encouragement of your partner, the very things that make a partnership."[7]

---

7. Joy A. Glenner et al., *When Your Loved One Has Dementia: A Simple Guide for Caregivers* (Baltimore: The Johns Hopkins University Press, 2005), 37.

Right! Here comes one of the worst nightmares Jane and I could ever have imagined, and our strongest deterrent, our time-tested relationship, begins to morph and shift under us. Now I'm reading about "child-proofing" electrical outlets and "Problems Meeting Goals of Continence Care."

What next?

The chapter ends with another story. A woman, Olivia, whose sister Yvette is pretty far along the dementia continuum, invites Yvette to move in with her. Here's an excerpt:

> Once Yvette adjusted to the new situation, it appeared that Olivia's dining room was going to be one of her favorite places. She liked to sit at one side of the dining room table and look out the large window across the room. She usually fiddled with the small objects Olivia had on display on the buffet or rummaged in the buffet to look for things to hold and move about. . . . [Olivia] added other things that Yvette liked to the buffet drawers and shelves: yarn, fabric squares, colorful magazines, postcards, costume jewelry. She changed the items frequently so that Yvette had new things to examine.[8]

OK, now reread the story and imagine that the part of Yvette, the demented human, was instead played by an inquisitive, spoiled, curious, sensuous *cat*. As Yvette, a cat would know just how to go about finding the perfect spot in the sun while inscrutably taking in this whole wide world we all share.

There is so much to learn about wonder and mystery from a cat.

Maybe I can turn into one?!

---

8. Glenner, 80.

SKY: NEURO-OP

Ever heard of a neuro-ophthalmologist?

Well, I know I hadn't, until the day I needed one.

The family upright piano, originally purchased for my Aunt Mary Ellen's piano lessons in the 1920s (or some other ancient time), was making its way back around to me. I'm not much of a player, but I do enjoy making most of the sounds that come out when I sit down at the bench and give the keys a whack. It also felt fortuitous that I was getting a turn at the instrument now, what with all the stories that inevitably arise about "breakthroughs" and "mysterious connections" that people living in (primarily) the end stages of Alzheimer's can experience with exposure to live music.

The Alzheimer's angle was less on my mind than the opportunity to sit down and play again, whenever I wanted to.

Imagine my surprise when the delivery day turned out to be less than exciting. I'd dug through the sheet music I'd been carrying around since forever, picked out some pieces I might be able to get through, and prepared to play. I arranged the music, sat down on the bench, adjusted the tails of my swallowtail coat, waited for the rapt concertgoers to hush—just kidding . . .

Once I glimpsed the keyboard, I knew that my long-awaited return to the piano was a bust. The keys refused to line up. Instead, I saw only a pile of white, with occasional random thin black lines. It was my long-term memory that came to the fore, telling me I was seeing the eighty-eight keys in a hopeless jumble. And, yes, those were my real-life fingers and hands at the top of the pile.

What was missing were the connections. I could understand the notes on the page in front of me. I could imagine or remember what sounds to expect when I hit the keys. But my brain was overwhelmed. I tried closing one eye. I tried closing the other eye. Best, I tried closing both eyes! Better piano players than I don't need music. Just a few scribbles about keys and chords can keep many musicians busy for hours.

I had an appointment coming up with my regular eye doctor, so I decided to ask him about it. He had no clue, and recommended a local neuro-ophthalmologist. I learned that this specialty practice is designed to deal with eye and vision abnormalities that may have fallen through the cracks of mainstream ophthalmology. Accordingly, a sign at the check-in desk warns that initial visits are at least two hours long. Good thing I have time on my hands, as Dr. A. runs me through his mill and writes a lengthy report on the long and short of my visual systems. Like my other tests, it's more about what I *don't* have rather than what I *do* have. He is willing to venture that my problem with the errant keys is simply a matter of "mental confusion" somehow related to my "memory problem."

"Sorry, there's nothing else to be done."

My super-dilated eyes drip an extra tear or two when he reports that he found a small cataract on each eye, too small to worry about right now. Does he know that my life expectancy just took a nosedive of ten years or so, making baby cataracts the least of my worries?

SKY: **LOST ON THE TRAIN**

How do you get lost on a train? Well, *you* probably don't get
lost on a train. Most people don't. Or maybe they get lost
trying to find the right train. Or they get mixed up trying
to find the right station to get off. I could manage either of
these any time, but it takes major moron skills to get lost
on a moving express train. How did I do it? Pretty easily
actually . . .

Step one: get tired.
Jane and I board the Vermonter, Amtrak's direct train from
northern Vermont to New York City, at 9:45 a.m. Our final
destination: Edison, somewhere in central New Jersey, eleven hours later.

It turns into a long, long day. Nothing wrong with the
train. The train is almost always a good time.

Step two: go underground.
Our itinerary requires us to change trains at Penn Station in
New York City, and ride on a New Jersey Transit train for
a final hour to get to our destination. This is where things
start to get weird. We get off the train along with the other
passengers and step off onto the station platform. It turns
out that those platforms have not been renovated since they
were built in 1904. It is dim and dark down there. We follow the crowd up a set of escalators that bring us up a few
floors, but still underground, to a waiting area I don't remember from other trips. No natural light. No air. I have to
squint to read the signs.

Jane shifts into high gear and goes on a quest for tickets and info about the next train. Tickets are available by shoving money into a slot in the wall, and Jane quickly takes care of business, no other humans involved. The next train leaves in just a few minutes. We tumble down more narrow walkways and stairs, heading for who knows what. Once again, Jane has everything right, and there is a *long* train waiting to leave at yet another grimy platform. A conductor is blowing her whistle and shouting for us to get onboard. I stop and admire the setting, imagining how perfect it would be for a European WWII movie. Just add some steam, cigarette smoke, and fedoras . . . Jane gives me a glare and a shove, and we are on the train as it begins to move. Perfect!

Step three: stay in the dark.
The slick electric commuter train we are now on is as different from the long-distance Amtrak as a smartphone is to a clunky "modern" phone of the 1950s. It whips out of the station, getting up to speed in a flash. Prerecorded announcements give occasional muddy info about the next stop. There is no map of the train's route. I guess you're just supposed to know. The windows are huge, but the lights flashing chaotically by just emphasize how ungrounded we all are, zooming along through the dark.

Step four: read an exciting book.
Jane goes for a walk. When she returns, she notes that it's a long train. I nod and get back to my book.

Step five: lose track of time and space.
After a (long, medium, or short) while, a walk begins to
sound like a good idea, and besides I have to pee, so after a
quick consult with Jane, I head out the way she has returned.
Luckily, just as I leave our car, I pick up a pen from the floor,
and I find the presence of mind to write our car number on
my hand. Soon, I quickly discover another bewildering fea-
ture of this train: every car is a clean, shiny plastic car that
looks identical to every other clean, shiny plastic car! And
every clean, shiny plastic car is a double decker, with stair-
ways at each end. This means that each car has double the
seating and a whole different set of passengers depending on
if I'm walking on the upper or lower level. Uh-oh . . .

I walk, and walk some more. Very quickly, I'm disorient-
ed. Soon after, I'm completely at a loss. Even though the cars
are identical, if I turn around and walk the other way, the
passengers may or may not be the same depending which
level I'm on. After traversing some more cars, and going
up (or maybe down) a level or two, I finally see something
different: two conductors—actual humans! NJ Transit must
be saving labor costs, because these two appear to be the
only conductors on the whole train. No dining car, no café
car, no lounge car, no baggage car. Just clean, shiny, plastic,
identical cars.

I ask the conductors if they could please direct me to the
nearest restroom, and they just look at each other, which I
take to be not a good sign. After a few more silent looks,
one points in the direction I just came from and directs a
silent look my way, ending the conversation. Given the condition of my bladder, I'm sure I would have noticed a bathroom if I'd passed one.

This leaves me with some unattractive options:

- The conductors are messing with me.
- They don't know where the bathroom is.
- There is no bathroom.

I square up my shoulders, thank the conductors, and head out in the opposite direction of their advice. As I leave them, I pick up my pace. Soon I'm moving sturdily down (or up) the train. It is impossible to know which way is forward or back, and besides, after standing a while, trying to figure out (unsuccessfully) which way is which, I don't remember which way I was going when I stopped or when I started, so by now I am totally turned around. Since I can't rally any brain cells to help me with my decision, I just pick a direction and a level and go.

After a (small, medium, or large) number of cars, I stumble upon . . . my conductor pals again. I'm pretty sure I entered their car from the opposite direction than I left it, but my memory is on break. Then I remember the scribbles on my hand. With as much confidence as I can muster, I ask him if he could direct me to car no. 105783. Watch out! Here comes the look again!! He goes to another car, with me in close pursuit, pushes a button, and unfolds a giant door. The compartment behind the door looks to be the brains of the train. Fortunately, it's working a lot better than mine this evening. The silent conductor plugs a laptop computer into something in there, nods, and with a final silent look my way heads down (or up) the train. With my remaining senses on full alert, I stick close to the conductor.

Like a small child, I am terrified of the consequences of losing the adult in charge. I'm smart enough to realize how easily I could pass Jane's position on the train by taking the wrong level. And dumb enough to lose my sense of direction alone in a strange place.

I follow my hero silently, looking at each passenger as we pass by. Soon, we come across the loveliest sight in the world: Jane, steadily knitting along like nothing bad could happen. Home at last!

ALZHEIMER'S CANYON
Episode #5

[In case you have forgotten, our traveler's detour has turned from bizarre to frightening. Somehow, he has been flushed into Alzheimer's Canyon itself, where survival seems questionable.]

There's that rumbling again. Louder. No way can this turn out anywhere near good. Even if I can stay on this wall a little longer, it will only be until the next San-Di-Flush peels me off and does who-knows-what with me.

"Help! I need help!" I'm screaming now. "Isn't there anyone here?"

"Well, ahm here, buddy. And y'all don't need to shout," says a soft, Southern voice.

"Who . . . where . . . what are you? What do I do?"

"That's a lot of questions from someone out on the ragged edge. Is there any particular order you'd like 'em answered? Just in case you run out of time, I mean," the voice answers.

"Wh-where can I be safe?"

"Too late for safe—you goin' Down, buddy. You gonna hang on for me to get to your other questions? Ah got time."

"Owww," is all I can manage to say.

"I believe y'all's first question is, Who am I. That's a deep one. Since we may be a little pressed for time, how 'bout I just tell you my name for the present? It's Rhodes, Dusty Rhodes. Question number two: Where am I. That's easy, same place as you, the edge of Alzheimer's Canyon. You jest ain't seeing me! Question number three: What am I. Now y'all gettin' deep agin. And from y'all's squirmin', I think I gotta give you the short-short version: Ahm an ageless self. You cain't see me because ah don't have a body no more. Don't need it, nor a mind neither. All those years watchin' that mind and that body growing stronger, cleverer—if ah don't mind sayin' so—then, like everyone else around here, watchin' 'em shrink . . . shrink to no more no less than a turkey turd. Well, since this is the short version, I'll save you the details, but I decided along the way that I didn't want to return to the beautiful pile where we all started with the final breath, like everyone else do. Now, didn't you have one more question?"

"Yes, yes! What do I do now?"

"A very good question, and sadly, no time for an in-depth talk. No time, because you goin' Down, pal. A little advice: don't even try to hang on that sand-slippery wall no more. You can't go back and you know it. Let it go, buddy. It's simple . . . you are goin' Down."

I release my claws on the sandy stone and, in an instant—Down . . . away from everything I can see (and can't see!). Down, as the chaos ramps up all around me. Down . . . trying to keep my head above the choking mess roaring at me from everywhere. Down . . .

At long, long last the roaring and the falling ease off, and with amazement I realize again: I'm not dead yet. I try to dust myself off a bit, but that's pretty much hopeless. The dust is settling everywhere, including right where I am . . . wherever *that* might be.

Time to take stock, yet again. Once again, I pass the wiggle test. Nothing obviously broken. Never mind that up and down seem about the same difference in this choking smog. I remember feeling the sweaty palms of panic as I tried so desperately to cling to that wall seconds ago. Then the depthless terror of letting go, abandoning myself to whatever grisly end was in store for me.

Why do I have no idea where in the world I am?

And was that just today that I took that miserable detour that landed me in this miserable sandbox?

"Now, that warn't so bad, war it, cowboy?"

SKY: FUNNY, YOU DON'T *LOOK* LIKE YOU HAVE ALZHEIMER'S

If I don't look like, or act like, the Alzheimer's picture in your brain, maybe it's time for a second look. Both at my brain and at yours! Because I *know* something untoward is going on in my set of 100 billion neurons.

So, let's try a brain check:

"How's it going in there, Sky-Brain?"

"Not too bad, you?"

"Not bad, but people are talking."

"Talking about what now?" Sky's Brain wants to know.

"Oh, the usual, everything and nothing. It seems there is not much agreement about how I am (I should say, we!) are progressing on this Alzheimer's thing. I mean, a friend just told me I seemed to be in my 'right mind.' Weird, huh?"

"Yeah, you got that right. Maybe they've never seen world-class juggling before. I got 100 billion balls in the air here, trying to fight off a no-win assault. And did I really just hear you use the word *progress* to refer to this slow-motion train wreck? That's the end of my life, and your life, you're discussing so blithely. Have a little respect for your partner, pal. And I should care about this 'lack of agreement' . . . why? We've been over and over this. Like the song says, 'Nobody know nuttin'!!' The neurologist know nuttin'! The social worker know nuttin'! The researchers know nuttin'! The experts know nuttin'! NOBODY KNOW NUTTIN'! And this is one pissed-off Brain you are talking to."

"Easy, old fellah, you're getting all worked up again . . .

Listen to me. I agree with you 100 percent. I've just been noticing that, with all the ignorance, people are getting busy filling in the gaps any way they feel like. Maybe they're just as scared as you and I are. But . . . it's really not our problem if they're scared. And it's not our problem if their pictures of us are distorted. We got to live through every day. And, no, I'm not in my 'right mind.' I'm in *my* mind."

Isn't that enough?

. . . .

SKY: WTF

My watching self wonders what's up as I stand in a corner holding my head in two hands.

My deeper self, now shaking and watching the floor, doesn't have to wonder: it sets off the alarm, at first a discreet beep and a small warning light, increasing in volume and intensity if ignored.

World Triage Filter   World Triage Filter   World Triage Filter

World Triage Filter   World Triage Filter

World Triage Filter   World Triage Filter
World Triage Filter
World Triage Filter
World Triage Filter
World Triage Filter

World Triage Filter

World Triage Filter

What, you may ask, is this "WTF" business? The short (and completely un-medical) answer is that it's the critical part of our brain that evaluates and tries to make sense of all the incoming information from the hyper-complex outside world.

Triage in times of crisis.

Steadiness as we move through our days.

Strength to keep psychosis at bay.

And, yes, WTF monitors our interactions with the whole entire world, as well as our internal reactions as we do so. Important job.

When my filter is working only intermittently, I lose its vital services of screening, sorting, prioritizing, and generally working with incoming data. Here's an example: The other day the discussion at the dinner table drifted to money and finances for some reason. It wasn't a heated or a difficult conversation, yet I soon heard the beeps and flashing lights from the WTF. For some reason, my filter was not available to modulate as the background noise somehow got turned up and up, and in the end, it was all I could hear.

I haven't really got much to complain about because most of the time my inner filter works just like it always has, humming along in the background.

But when that filter isn't reliably doing its thing, my brain is working with a budget flip phone, not the latest smartphone. Every incoming message interrupts the processing of the whole unit, instead of discreetly passing along a text for me to deal with when the time is right. A metaphorical smartphone could also help by acting as a conduit to bring in more information to help sort through a problem, or at the least provide some comfortable music or maybe a cat video to take the edge off.

I'm coming to see that one of my regular chores ought to be monitoring that oh-so-important WTF to extend its useful life:

Keep it clean and fresh; no crud.

Work out a regular plan for time off to recharge.

Avoid unscheduled shutdowns.

. . . .

SKY: TAKING THE TEST, AGAIN

I had a long-delayed visit to the Memory Clinic the other day, the second follow-up visit since the diagnosis back in the summer of 2016. Due to scheduling conflicts, I'm overdue for another cognitive assessment and check-in. I ask the friendly psychometrist if the test will be the same as the last time. She just gives me an inscrutable smile and says, "Partly," as she leads me into her office. A former mediator myself, I admire her skills at acting neutral and generally keeping her cool as she guides me through the bizarre world of her test.

The first question sets the stage: "I am going to give you three words for you to remember and then say back to me."

OK, pretty straightforward.

Board

Flag

[a simple word I still don't remember]

Just as soon as she gives me the words, she looks at me to repeat them. Boy, this is going to be easy . . . until I start to try. All I can come up with is "board"—I was concentrating and everything. I even did a little mnemonic with "board" and "flag," thinking of the game capture the flag. I guess I thought of it a little too hard, because I completely forgot the third word—as well as "flag."

Train wreck of the brain.

Just like blanking out on finding $6.41 at the store.

And this is just the first word! At this rate, it will be a long afternoon.

It wasn't, though. A lot of word questions followed, which I did well on, but no clocks to draw, which was too bad because I can whip out a nice clock now in under a minute in whatever style you choose: Roman numerals, regular numerals, no numerals. Give me just a little extra time, and I bet I could produce a fair grandfather's model. With a similar amount of practice, I've now become a whiz at making change, probably at least as good as I was in third grade.

My memory lapses now are unpredictable and unexpected and embarrassing. In the meantime, I can only guess or imagine the next to go:

My phone number.

My zip code.

My cat's name.

When to change the oil.

* * *

Back at the memory clinic, I am scheduled to meet with Dr. P. to discuss my "progress" with dementia—or, more accurately, dementia's progress with me. As I pass the psychometrist's office, I notice Dr. P. in there. I ask if he has the results of the test. "Oh, yes. I have your results," he lets me know with a smile. (Not *the* results, but *my* results). I know intuitively how much I have slipped since my last visit. I'm forgetting the names of some things and some people, and much as I love reading, my comprehension is spottier than it was. Don't even think about asking me to do simple math! I'm more easily confused by instructions.

On the test I couldn't remember today's date (oops, I should have practiced!). I started with the year because I was pretty clear on that, but when I got to the number I was off by two. Counting backward from one hundred by sevens was almost too hard, and when I got to seventy-nine, I asked if that was enough, and the psychometrist smiled and said, "No, keep going." Sigh. At least she didn't ask me who was president!

Then why was Dr. P. smiling?

Because I did so well!! My score was, once again, just one level below the last time, which was also just behind its previous test. In short, Dr. P. was beaming because my decline, though steady, was in a range he was happy with. But I was not happy. The questions I got wrong were "easy" . . . there was a blank spot in there that scared me. I wonder when the blank spot will get bigger and/or multiply.

Dr. P. has one hell of a job: Monitoring hundreds of patients and families through a one-way journey ending in death.

No cure.

Thankfully, my own reaction is more complex. I'm working on living. Living as fully and joyfully as I can, blank spots be damned.

SKY: FIVE AND A HALF MILLION

Five and a half million.

5,500,000 is a *lot*.

It is the estimated number of people living with dementia right now in the United States, according to the Alzheimer's Association.

The number is a lot, but where is everybody?

Well, "common sense" (or stereotype) tells us to look for the demented among us in nursing homes and other long-term care facilities. I looked and found that over a million and a half Americans are currently living in nursing homes, and another million in assisted living. It is estimated that roughly 50 percent of these residents are on the dementia continuum. So nursing homes and assisted living facilities account for 1.25 million of the total 5.5 million directly affected by dementia, as estimated by the Alzheimer's Association. What are the remaining four million-plus people with dementia up to? Where do they live?

These are not just idle questions; the dementia numbers are skyrocketing. Since 2000, deaths from heart disease, the most common cause of death in the U.S., have *decreased* 14 percent. Deaths from dementia have *increased* 89 percent. A new case is diagnosed every sixty-six seconds! Think about it: Most of the people currently living with dementia do not live in residential care. Most continue to live at home. My personal plan A is to live at home just as long as humanly possible, spending my remaining time with family, friends, and good times, mixed up of course with familiar doses of confusion and fear.

I know, I know . . . it's not just up to me; my care partners must have their lives too. But gradually the real world of work is catching up with the real lives of working families. Even the federal government is realizing the importance of family leave time off for family members to tend to major family issues like dementia care.[9]

But back to those five and a half million of us living with dementia in this country. Most of us are *not* confined to an institution. We are everyday people. We grocery shop, go to the movies, enjoy what we enjoy. We take risks sometimes, just like everyone else.

How many people on the dementia continuum have you passed by on the street today? How many have you said hello to?

---

9. https://www.dol.gov/general/topic/workhours/fmla

SKY: READY, SET . . . SLOW

I've done what I'm supposed to do (at least the steps I can remember!):

- Visited a lawyer to update my will.
- Completed an advance directive and a durable power of attorney for health care, should my body outlast my brain's ability to communicate my wishes about medical care.
- I've kept myself busy, volunteering here, there, and everywhere.
- I've spent more and deeper time with friends and family.
- Spent quality time in the woods, on weekly guided nature walks led by faculty at the UVM Field Naturalist Program.
- Started riding my beloved bike more, now that the weather has started to break.
- Advocated for a support group for those living with dementia, then joined one when it became available.
- Traveled coast-to-coast and north-to-south by train and only got lost twice.
- Read and wrote like crazy, learning and sharing about my Alzheimer's experience.
- With Jane, created a twenty-minute sermon about dementia which was presented at thirteen church services across the Northeast, with more scheduled into the summer.

Wow, now that I write this list, I remember I've been a busy boy!

It takes a lot of work and a lot of time to keep ahead of the threats of early Alzheimer's. There can be a new twist every day. As much as I have read, and talked with fellow travelers on the Alzheimer's detour, as much as I have tried to figure it all out, to "learn my way out of this," I keep coming up against limits. Planning can only take us so far. And how many new miracle diets can we stand?!

Here's what happened to me: I was innocently sweeping out my castle—actually, slowly reading a 975-page book by Ken Follett about castles. Follett was mansplaining exactly how castles were designed to protect a small number of otherwise under-defended people from conventional military threat. As weapons became more destructive, castles became more massive and impregnable, deterrents in their own rights. Then more destructive weapons were developed. And on and on, ending, and not ending, in the arms race of current times. Follett tells a detailed story of how a handful of clever, stealthy, and motivated attackers manage to overrun a complacent armed group that had put a little too much faith in the seeming invincibility of a castle.

I looked up from my sweeping and saw an enemy I had heard of but not yet encountered. A white fog was creeping up the grassy hill opposite, burying all the vegetation from view.

Did I say it was creepy? Yes, I did.

I move higher up in the castle. The sun is still shining up here. Down below, the fog continues swirling, slowly climbing my way.

"Pull up that drawbridge, Sky," I order myself. "The outside stairway too! I don't care if it's the only way out."

I don't know what this stuff is, but I know for sure I don't want it touching me. Now that it's closer, I can see that it's not really white. At least not what you would call *white-*white. Is there such a word as dirty-white?

All the moisture serves to bring out the smells in the castle, which were considerable. Formerly dead and dry things are now slimy dead and rotting things. There is no way to get away. All my defenses are useless against the stinking slime. My defenses only serve to stop me from getting away.

And, in the meantime, the noxious fog is working its way into every nook and cranny of the castle and into every crevice of my body, my precious brain included.

There is absolutely no way to do anything that would make my world any more disgusting. I am at the highest point of the castle now, and I'm choking back vomit. There is nothing I can do. I don't have the energy for anything, and besides there is no point.

I'm not surprised that Dr. Alzheimer has chosen to play the depression card. I've been pretty upbeat for a while now. I just didn't expect it to be so grim and hopeless.

. . . .

SKY: ALL-PURPOSE SLURS

I remember back in elementary school, in the 1950s, we students had a rich variety of racist and homophobic jokes. (This was in addition to a constant crop of fart and booger jokes.) I'm not remembering the content of the actual jokes right now—probably a blessing—but I do remember the structure.

Q. Why did the [pick random ethnic group] do [such-and-such dumb thing]?

The point of the joke was that it made fun of whatever ethnic group came to mind, hopefully without getting me beaten up by the huge Italian guy as I try out another joke at his expense.

Half the time, I never knew what the words meant anyway. They were basically interchangeable. Take your pick. Mix and match. Whichever you pick, it means the same: My group is better than every other group because . . . well, uh, just because.

Here's an old-people-are-dangerous-joke that I think is pretty funny:

"Isn't it a blessing that Grandpa died peacefully in his sleep, unlike all his passengers, screaming in terror?"

I've noticed that there is a large subset of negative words relating to cognitive functioning, words that most of us use freely every day. How do these words sound to you: *stupid, dumb, moron, out there, not playing with a full deck, pretty far gone, half there, crazy, simple, mindless, simple-minded, idiotic, dull, lame-brained, demented, not the sharpest knife in the drawer.*

What is the purpose of using these words? What are we trying to say when we say them? We might be discussing someone's neurological diagnosis, but probably not.

Stupid movie. Idiotic plot. Crazy idea. Despite the hurtful, pejorative nature of all these words, they are, by and large, acceptable when talking about, or even talking with, people on the dementia continuum, or anyone else we want to feel superior to.

So out of it. This double standard is hurtful and helps no one. It helps us forget that dementia is a disability that we humans need to accommodate, just like the many other disabilities we are working hard to accommodate.

But it's a long road. Just google "dumb blonde jokes" for a rough idea of how far we have to go.

SKY: AT LEAST I KNOW

Last night I was visited by an Alzheimer's factoid so simple and haunting that it wouldn't let me sleep. It was passed on by Meryl Comer in her memoir, *Slow Dancing with a Stranger*, her story of caring for first her husband, and then her mother, both with very high-needs Alzheimer's dementia. Hers was a harrowing journey of well over twenty years of nonstop, sometimes simultaneous, home care for two very difficult family members. Protected by his good-old-boy colleagues, her husband, a world renowned scientist mentor to scores of fellow scientists and researchers, went undiagnosed for years. In the meantime, his personality changed disturbingly, and he became physically and emotionally abusive and paranoid.

Non-demented readers may remember that I started this story alluding to a troubling bit of Alzheimer's trivia, and now what am I doing telling this whole other story?

Good point! I can only answer that the various pieces

make some sense to me so far, and I'd like to ask your indulgence to listen as I try filling in some blanks.

OK, so what's the factoid already?

Comer lets us know matter-of-factly:

Only 50 percent of people directly affected by dementia are ever diagnosed![10]

Why does this make a difference?

Try imagining your brain ever-so-slowly, imperceptibly, becoming unreliable. Your friends, colleagues, family members, coworkers, act like strangers. You have to check your phone to know the year and day of the week. They look at you strangely, criticize irrationally. You can't figure out the restaurant bill for some completely unknown reason. The whole world is strange, every day.

Not to mention surprise visits that occur now on a daily basis, without warning.

I've had enough practice by now to know how freaky this is of a way to live. And I have the support of family and friends. I know that my brain is coming apart, and it's slow and painless. At least I have knowledge and support to figure it out and try to ride out the roughest waters.

I really can't begin to imagine the alternative . . . having the world and all its bits and pieces turn on me, no longer safe, no longer at home!

No better way to define terror.

---

10. Meryl Comer, Slow Dancing with a Stranger: Lost and Found in the Age of Alzheimer's (New York: HarperOne, 2014), 4.

ALZHEIMER'S CANYON
Episode #6

Yet again, the dust settles . . .

Yet again, I seem to remain alive, so . . .

Yet again, I run through my now-familiar, completely nonprofessional wiggle check and overall physical assessment.

Yet again, I confirm that I remain sore but alive, with one major change: The San-Di-Flush has obliterated all signs of my clothing! Nothing left. Nada. I'm as naked as the day I was born. Man, isn't this the icing on the cake? Am I supposed to just walk up to people and casually start a conversation, buck naked? Not in my world.

My disembodied friend will have some fun with me now. I know I would, if the tables were turned. But, luckily, I don't see him anywhere right now. "What? Wait, you stupid dumbbell," I chide myself. "Don't hold your breath waiting to see an invisible redneck who probably doesn't even have a neck. Use your head, dumbass!!"

"Oh, yeah, right," I tell myself, making an effort to settle down. OK, once again . . . where am I? In a sandbox, on a mega-scale? Where pebbles are boulders and boulders are massifs? In the haziness of the mid-distance, I spot what might be the sandy cliff I scattered down to get here.

This is when I notice some other people in the near distance. People! Not that I've been doing so well with human encounters since I got on this godforsaken detour, but I have to check them out. How else am I going to get out of this nightmare? I head over in their direction.

I don't get far before a swarthy woman jumps into my path. Some kind of white nurse's outfit covers her formidable muscles. My guess is she brooks no ill behavior.

"HONEY, HONEY, *THERE* YOU ARE!!" she screeches in that extra loud, extra slow, halfway musical voice reserved for toddlers. "Oh my my . . . Did we lose something, dear?" She grins, pointing at my crotch as I cover myself as best I can with my two hands. "Where's your johnny?"

Is this outrageous woman talking about my privates?! What gives her the right? Give me a break. Deciding to keep to the high road, I look down my nose at her and sniff, "Excuse me, my . . . johnny . . . ? I don't know who you are, or what you are talking about, but even if I did, the location of my 'johnny,' as you call it, is none of your business," I offer as aloofly as possible, while still clutching between my legs with as much dignity as I can muster.

"Well. Now, if we are getting all high and mighty, Gramps, I would remind you that *every* johnny worn by every resident of Shady Way Home is the property of Shady Way Home and is not yours to strip off for whatever demented reason strikes your bizarre fancy.

"Hun, you were wearing it when you wandered off, and I don't see it now. Where's that johnny? You can't be doing this, dear! Now, walk this way," she commands, swinging sternly around and marching toward the other people. I try to resist the urge to swing my butt, copying her sturdy sashay, as we make our way back to the others.

(This place is playing tricks on me. I said "back to the others." Like I've been there before. Yeah, right! And that nurse acted like she already knew me. No way, Jose . . .)

When we finally make it back to the others, I notice a group of old folks playing in the sand with miniature shovels and pails. They look at me with mild interest, then at the direction of Nurse Ratched, they get back to work.

I also notice they are all wearing the same outfit: A lightweight nightie that snaps up the back. A few are wearing what looks like diapers underneath. Weird, or what?

There's a second nurse, and the two of them start in talking as if I were completely invisible. (Maybe I was?!)

"Can you believe it? He was out in the quadrant stark-jumping naked. Naked!! Ugly as the day is long!"

"God, these geezers give me the creeps every day!"

"Of course, we got no backup johnnys, just our first aid kit . . ."

"I know! Wrap some tape around that ugly butt, and call it good."

"Sounds like a lot of work . . . and then we gotta pull it all off when we get back to the Home? Ugh!

Wai! Wai!! We got any empty diapers left?"

"Yeah, but we don't know if he needs 'em . . ."

"He needs 'em if we say he needs 'em!"

"Hah! You right!"

"OK, hun. You ever worn these before?" she says to me, holding up a plastic monstrosity. "Just lay down here. Now!"

"Wait a minute. Wait a minute!" I protest.

"Look, baby, the more you fuss, the longer it takes. And I know for a fact that neither of us has extra time for shenanigans. So let's go!"

SKY: LONG TIME

Long time, no write.

Is something wrong?

Nope, mostly I've been enjoying living in the present in summer mode, even though it means sharing time with my all-too-constant companion, Professor Alzheimer.

This is my sixty-eighth New England summer, give or take a few, and I'm getting used to the routine by now. A routine of no routine. Bits and pieces of every weather, as the natural world warms around and within us. Swimming. Yet another building project.

We've just made it through another record-breaking bout of hazy, hot, and humid, while a couple of weeks ago on the radio, they warned us of "scattered frost in the cold pockets of the Northeast Kingdom." The fierceness of the most recent relentless heat events no doubt made worse by human activities.

Should we discuss the end of the natural world?

Or perhaps today's weather . . . ?

Here's another idea: How about yet another glimpse at our uninvited guest, Professor A., and his entourage?

I recently heard from a friend of a friend, call her Sarah, someone I hadn't yet met in person who was more than a little disturbed about her recent Alzheimer's diagnosis and was generally trying to make sense of her new world.

Sarah and I shared familiar fears:

We'd been overwhelmed by the losses that we imagined ahead of us. A certain grimness was beginning to feel normal.

We both worried about the changes ahead in our identities, literally who we are, while the incurable disease runs its course.

As the attacks on our intellects and memory continue, we feared changing into people neither we nor our loved ones would value spending time with. How can we not become strangers? What is left for us if the glue of memory no longer holds our selves together?

Isolation and loneliness may come to star in the time we have left, as our social selves deteriorate.

We might lose our lifelong interest in learning new things, appreciating clever songs or jokes.

Our lives will continue their inevitable decline into a disastrous train wreck.

This is a nightmarish list of disastrous outcomes, and it's only just a generic beginning. I'll bet that each of the millions of people living with dementia can add nightmares of their own as they contemplate their futures.

Yet a deeper look reveals many of our shared nightmares to be possibilities, not carved-in-stone inevitabilities. Ironically, I can still vividly remember the times, more than a year or so ago now, when I could not get through a day without tears.

Every day!

I was involuntarily visited by my Loss List, with unhappy results.

Then, one day, I dimly began to realize that the disintegration Sarah and I feared so much was still in the future . . . Perhaps far in the future! Perhaps not to happen at all!

A blessing and a curse of the Alzheimer's path is its slow speed, at least for me. For many of us on the dementia continuum, especially those with younger onset, we have way more than enough time to consider where the path might lead us.

Letting the vocabulary shift from "will" to "might" is a huge step. Who says Sarah or I will die because we've forgotten how to chew or swallow or breathe? Or that we will wind up living only in shadow shells of our "true selves." Sure, that could happen. But so could a horrendous traffic accident on the way to the neurologist appointment next month.

Let's keep the present and the future in their proper places and *live* in the meantime.

So, what do I want to do with my time left?

What do *you* want to do with yours?

THE HALLUCINATIONS BEGIN

This was the year of the big changes. Sky's anxiety and frustration exploded, leaving him little energy for much else. He hated participating in the house building project at the lake, and began to stay home. He wanted it done, so he didn't have to think and worry about it anymore. Sayer quit his job in September to help me finish the house and help take care of Sky. With Emma's return at the end of the month, she joined the crew. They worked hard on interior finish work—doors, trim, flooring—and tackled the siding. With the basics done, Dana, Sayer, and Emma threw a New Year's Eve party to usher in 2019.

We came up with a new working phrase: "Sky is always right—even when he isn't." We learned to work with whatever Sky thought, and would redirect, play improv, or soothe, depending on what he said. I created a big sign, "Everything is OK unless you are told otherwise," that he kept on his bedside table. His short-term memory was gone, so I got a whiteboard where I listed the date, day of the week, and activities for the day. He could no longer figure out what clothes to wear, so I began choosing his daily outfits, and as time went on, I had to help him put them on. He stopped driving of his own accord—thank goodness—because it scared him. Finding the bathroom at night began to be a challenge, so I installed night-lights. By the time we got to our final "Living with Dementia" worship service in September, it was clear that he was unable to do that anymore. Perfect timing.

My brother was diagnosed with esophageal cancer in November, and I took a week to visit him in Florida. Even though Sayer, Emma, and Dana watched out for Sky, it was obvious I could no longer go away for any extended period of time.

We got notice that DAA was planning another conference in Atlanta in June. Sky had begun participating in weekly Zoom meetings, sponsored by DAA, with other people with dementia, and seemed to be making friends. Sky suggested we apply to do a workshop, "Nurturing a Dementia-Friendly Spiritual Life." We were accepted, and we began to plan.

The cold Vermont winter settled in, and Sky said he wanted to go south for a respite from the Arctic air. He also wanted to volunteer on the Texas-Mexico border—this was at the peak of the Central American refugee crisis. I had already been planning on attending the Texas winter conference of my retired colleagues group later in February, so I agreed to the trip. We planned to visit my brother in Florida, stop in with friends in New Orleans, do the work on the border, and finally, attend the conference before making our leisurely way home. We—that is, I—would be driving. Luckily, I like long-distance driving.

The trip did not go well. Sky did not want to let me out of his sight—I could see it in his eyes which said, "Don't leave me." As we had done on many trips before, we would stop and play disc golf as a break from being in the car. Sky no longer had the energy to play eighteen holes—he barely had the energy for nine. Volunteering at a Catholic Charities refugee site in McAllen, Texas, was a challenge for him. Our job was to sit in the "baby room" bagging up a day's worth of formula and diapers to give to people with small children before they headed out to connect with family. Even that was confusing for Sky, and after one and a half hours each day he was done and ready for a nap. For all the challenges and hassles, at least we were warm!

We made our way from McAllen to the conference site outside of San Antonio. We were both down with colds—it seemed that most of the refugees were sick—so we happily collapsed in our room and went to sleep hoping to feel better in the next day. About five in the morning, Sky woke me up terrified that he was in the middle of a Mardi Gras parade and didn't want to be there. I blamed his hallucination on our high fevers, eventually calmed him down, and we both went back to sleep. (This is explained in greater detail later, in "The Incident.") I thought nothing of it, but the experience stayed with Sky, and continued to scare him so much that, on the last morning of the conference, he refused to participate. He wanted to go home right then, right now. Given that Vermont was a long way from Texas by car, I tried to convince him to fly. I would put him on a plane, and Dana or Sayer would pick him up at the other end. He was too scared to do that, so we hurriedly packed and hit the road. Five long days later, we were back home. I feared what would come next.

It didn't take long. As his nighttime hallucinations increased, so did his nighttime agitation, and early in March he fell out of bed, gashing his forehead on his bedside table. He clearly needed stitches, but I wasn't about to go to the emergency room in the middle of the night, so I patched him up, we went back to sleep, and we went to urgent care for five stitches once we were up and around. Sky was afraid of falling out of bed again, so he refused to sleep in our double bed. I dismantled the frame and put the mattress on the floor. That was fine as a temporary solution, but it was hard for both of us to get up off the floor. I went furniture shopping and bought a king-size mattress and bed frame that was eighteen inches off the floor instead of twenty-six. I bought new sheets, made a new quilt, and hoped the night-time problems were solved. It was not to be. Because our bedroom was too small to accommodate the bigger bed, we had to rearrange rooms. Sky was confused by the new loca-tion and the new bed. I had to help him into bed every eve-ning and whenever he returned after using the bathroom.

I loved being at the lake house, and thought I'd try hav-ing us live there part time, and part time in town. Unfor-tunately, that did not work for Sky. Transitions were hard on him, plus he fussed every time we were at the lake be-cause the siding wasn't finished. Driving back and forth was challenging for him as a passenger because he saw trouble around every corner—accidents waiting to happen, tractor trailers in the wrong lane, bad weather. His hallucinations were no longer just at night, but all day long as well. In town, the hallucinations were scary: cops, bad people, drug deals, theft, problems with the plumbing, problems with the cats or with Sayer and Emma. One night I caught him dressed and headed out the door—"Emma's hurt, I have to hurry"—and it took a long time to settle him down and back to bed. And, as was often the case, he would finally go back to sleep and I would lay there wide awake, wondering how much more I could take. I wondered if Sky had Lewy body dementia instead of Alzheimer's.

Fortunately, he had playful and enjoyable hallucinations at the lake house: sea lions and dolphins, Mardi Gras parties complete with food and music, nature elves and creatures cavorting in the fields.

In June, we headed back to Atlanta for the DAA conference and our workshop. That trip also did not go well. We'd planned a stop in Washington, DC, to visit the National Museum of African American History and Culture, but the crowds were too much for Sky, so we sat by a fountain all day and people-watched. It was frightening for me to leave him to go back to the hotel to fetch our luggage—he said he didn't have the energy to walk with me. Once at the conference, I expected Sky would want to hang out in person with his Zoom-group friends, but, no, he wanted to stay in the hotel room to watch Women's World Cup soccer. He was able to read his opening statement for the workshop— barely—but was unable to participate further. (Thankfully, I had another co-presenter, and it went well.) On the way home, we planned a stop in New York City for some theater. Again, Sky said no, and I could barely drag him out of the hotel room to get dinner. I was glad to get home. He was too.

Once again, I tried to find a therapist, and once again, no one clicked. But in March, I joined a monthly Zoom support group with some of my retired colleagues who were also caregivers, and that did the trick. I felt held by them, and looked forward to our monthly meetings to be able to speak freely and be listened to without judgement or interruption. It was just what I needed. Despite lack of sleep, between the support group, a small handful of friends, and my family, I felt I could keep on caring for Sky, no matter what.

SKY: **LET'S TALK ABOUT DEATH**

Part of living with a terminal condition is, well, living with a terminal condition. Those of us on the dementia continuum have an excuse to look ahead and imagine our final days and hours. We're on a special detour that leads only to death, right?

And as an excuse, it's not even a very good excuse. For many of us, myself included, our deaths feel closer now than before we made the acquaintance of Dr. Alzheimer. But it's a phony excuse because, last I heard, demented people aren't the only humans who will die at the end of our lives.

I would guess that most Americans could benefit from more contemplation of their mortality, rather than less. In this regard, many of us demented ones just might be a rare bit ahead of the game, if we've been paying attention.

I've just finished a fascinating new book, available at the library, about end-of-life options and choices, including for people living with dementia: *At Peace: Choosing a Good Death After a Long Life*, by Samuel Harrington, MD.[11] Dr. Harrington's not-so-radical observation after a thirty-plus-year career as a clinician (as well as having cared for his own parents) is that while most people express a desire to die peacefully at home with their loved ones, way too many become side-tracked by a medical system that repeatedly offers aggressive, often painful treatment options or tests "to buy a little time" or to give a new drug a try to forestall the inevitable.

---

11. Samuel Harrington, MD, *At Peace: Choosing a Good Death After a Long Life* (New York: Grand Central Life & Style, 2018).

Harrington reviews the five chronic diseases that cause over 90 percent of deaths in older people. He notes that "cause of death" is rarely as simple as a doctor choosing one of the Big Five. More realistically, there is a cascade of problems, each with its treatments, that weaken the body further, leaving the person vulnerable to further weakening, even if the treatment is "successful" as a short-term goal.

Here is Harrington's List:

- Congestive heart failure
- Cancer
- Chronic obstructive pulmonary disease (COPD)
- Dementia
- Diabetes mellitus (DM)

Harrington urges older people and their care partners to take a close look at treatment options as they develop a comprehensive plan for a loved one whose condition is serious. Do I always want to be resuscitated if my heart should stop beating? Do I want a feeding tube if I can't eat? Do I want a breathing tube if I am unable to breathe on my own? How much is enough?

Ever practical, Harrington suggests that if someone is plagued by two or more of the conditions on his list, they should think very carefully about adding (and treating) more.

And, how about this list? Notice any old friends?

Ole buddy Alzheimer's, of course, standing his ground with the other bullies.

A friend asked me the other day if I'd written anything lately. She hadn't seen a blog post for a while.

I assured her that she hadn't missed anything. I'd been busy with other things, what with summer and all. But, I said, I was working on a piece about death that I was having a good time with.

"Death?"

"Yeah! Death! Wha'd'ya think?"

"I think . . . I think I better check that my spice rack is still alphabetical."

Oh, OK. I get it. Who really wants to talk about death? Right? What a downer!

Loss, Sadness, More Loss.

Regret. Pain. Fear.

Right?

Nope.

Thinking about death is a gift—a gift to yourself and your family. To have the advance notice to make decisions, to talk about choices, to consider what makes for a good life—and a good death.

I've had the opportunity to let my family know my wishes about my care, now, before the stress of serious illness or injury intervenes. I have written down these wishes, with the help of a local attorney, in a legal document called an advance care directive, which is binding in all fifty states. In Vermont, my directive is instantaneously available to the staff in every hospital in the state.

I'm pleased.

Pleased to be on the same page as my family and care partners as the dreaded disease unfolds. Pleased that I don't have to worry about a medicalized death. Pleased to be able to live now, and not be concerned about what will happen at the end of my life.

JANE: CHANGES, CHANGES, AND MORE CHANGES

You try building a house with someone who has dementia, and see how it goes. Sky and I have built six houses together (along with many outbuildings), renovated two, and offered our services in New Orleans and the Gulf Coast helping people rebuild after Hurricane Katrina. All this work was challenging (especially my first time building!) and, in the end, very satisfying. To create something new, something beautiful, something useable, and something that will last, is great.

And we're at it again. Only this time, Sky can no longer take the lead, be the "contractor" holding all the pieces together, know what has to happen next. It's my turn.

And he can't do most of the carpentry tasks that he has done time and again, even long before I met him. He's frustrated (at times) and so am I.

The other day I realized that when I get angry about his inability to follow directions or anticipate the next task, I'm not just mad at him (for something he really has no control over), I'm mostly sad. Sad that he can't do these things anymore, sad that we've lost our beloved partnership in construction, sad that I'm the one who's solely responsible for this project. I don't want things to be like this.

But they are. And they will continue to be.

During my good moments, I marvel at what this disease has done, and what it hasn't yet done. Sky has lost his carpentry skills along with his common sense. His anxiety level escalates when a new activity is on the horizon, whether it is part of the house-building project or a long-anticipated event or an excursion out of town. Simple, daily tasks are getting more challenging.

Yet. His intellect remains as it has always been. He's passionate about keeping up with what's going on in the world (as depressing as much of that is) and having deep conversations about it. His care and commitment for people and animals remains strong. His love of the natural world (which was already very strong) has deepened. He's still busy doing crossword puzzles, reading, and writing, only being held back by the double vision that strikes him at times, and tiredness that hits him at odd moments. The song lyrics are still there, along with names of movies and movie stars, musicians, and titles of songs. (Stuff I can never remember!)

The brain is a mysterious thing.

When I remember to be, I am grateful for what is still good about all of this. When I don't remember, well, it's all pretty bleak. Every day is different—heck, every hour is different. I've always prided myself on my love of change and my ability to adapt to new circumstances, but this is challenging me to the max.

Thank goodness for my garden, my cats, and my daily swim after house building. It's the little things that give me strength.

(And, despite all this, the house is coming along!)

SKY: VOLUNTARY DRIVING BAN

Has it finally arrived: The end of my fifty-three-year driving career? And is "career" the right word? Yes, I think so.

I'm having no trouble at all remembering the excitement of the year I was fifteen, the year I came eligible to take the test for my learner's permit. For some reason, teenagers in Massachusetts had to wait, not until seventeen, not until sixteen—fifteen and a half was good enough.

The waiting was interminable, in any case. And besides, it felt like there was some kind of magic going on. One day I was too young to drive, and the next day all was OK. I just had to take a multiple-choice written test and a vision test, and then I could climb behind the wheel of the family's Chevy Impala, a tank of a vehicle if there ever was one. Is this really fair to the other drivers on the road? I mean, the ones who knew what they were doing out there? I had collected a lot of semi-useless book knowledge about cars and motors. I was all over my two magazine subscriptions (*Popular Mechanics* and *MAD*). Back then, I was able to identify every American car by its radiator and could tell you more than you needed or wanted to know about the evolution of tail-fin design and placement. And hood ornaments . . . fascination.

Fair or not fair, the process of getting behind the wheel rocked and split open my world. I remember realizing that my driveway was intimately connected to virtually every other road in all of North and South America. I just needed to make the correct turns and keep buying gas. Suddenly, my traveling options seemed boundless. Realistically, though, I wasn't going to buy all that gas. I didn't even have a car. But that didn't stop my horizons from expanding.

Then I stumbled upon a most elegant solution to the gas and car limitations: hitchhiking! Unfortunately, I can't remember my first ride, but it was the first of many hundreds of encounters that served to consistently define how I understood and appreciated this amazing world. I was the American boy, taking off in a car to find himself. It took over a decade for me to afford my own vehicle, but I got there, eventually parlaying my love of the roads and unpredictable adventures into paying work that involved a weekly round-trip truck route from northern Vermont to Boston and points in between.

Best of all, those roads led me to Jane, my amazing life partner and, now, care partner.

Making the transition to not driving should have been easier, though. I haven't noticed hood ornaments in decades. A car is no longer the key to enable access to a more wonderful world. A car is . . . a car.

But have I mentioned the hallucinations? How about the double vision? It doesn't happen all the time, but enough to get my attention.

The last time I drove, I slowed down for a pedestrian making her way across the city street. I tried to make eye contact as we met, but in the literal blink of an eye, she smiled . . . and vanished. When I got home, I told Jane that was my last time behind the wheel.

As time goes on, the hallucinations and double vision come more often. Here's an example: Sitting safely in the passenger seat, I notice two tractor-trailers right in front of me. They are shouldering side-to-side into each other, and

I can't understand how they can keep this up without one of them (at least) going in the ditch. Sure enough, the one on the right suddenly lurches rightward and plows through the woods without slowing a bit. The truck on the left is bashing and crashing into whatever is there to crash into on the interstate. I tense and try to ready myself for a fireball of disaster . . . which never materializes.

These experiences and others like them make it clear that my driving days are done.

Besides, Jane became the principal driver once Dr. Alzheimer came on the scene. Really, this change is another example of a practical, sensible adjustment to a permanent new reality.

Still, it hurts sometimes.

. . . .

SKY: DEMENTED LOGIC

A couple of weeks or so ago, I decided to plant some fall spinach in the garden. I had some space and the weather was still good. So, after checking with Jane, I bought some seeds and prepared a place for them. Because I remembered being forgetful lately(!), I carefully followed the planting directions on the packet, including marking the area with good-size stakes. Then I waited. And waited some more . . . and more. These brand-new seeds were just not coming up, despite frequent watering (I think) and good wishes. Not a single one! But I remember—I was so careful making my rows, laying the seeds in there, just like the package said to do.

Now, *think*, Sky. Rev those neurons up. What exactly do I remember doing?

Getting out the seed packet: yes.

Hoeing out the rows: yes.

Placing the seeds at the proper depth: yes.

Covering the seeds: ummm . . . no!

Now wait . . . maybe I did plant those seeds. I mean, it would make sense if I did. After all, I did the other steps (I think). But it would also make sense that I didn't.

After all, there was not a single spinach plant to show for it.

The memory trace for that short activity does not seem to be still available, if it ever was. If I try hard, can I call it up? No. Well, maybe.

Perhaps common sense, a cognitive skill now slowly but steadily dwindling away, can help. It used to, when I was faced with puzzles and mysteries.

The first step in applying common sense is to gather reliable data, paying particular attention to new or unusual or odd information. In the Case of the Missing Spinach, the fact that not even one of the seeds germinated might be important.

What else?

Well, I seem to "remember" several of the key parts of the story, nos. 1–3. I have a continuing set of thoughts I will call "remembering" these activities. And no. 4, a complete blank. (And watering? Not even on the list!)

Again, so what?

It felt like maybe I could trust my perceptions, my little memory of this little event—or more exactly, my non-memory of a non-event. I sure wanted it all to make sense. Logically, it could make some kind of sense . . . maybe . . . especially in a demented world.

Spanakopita, anyone?

ALZHEIMER'S CANYON
Episode #7

[When we last saw our intrepid traveler, he was in the midst of an awkward encounter with two employees of the Shady Way Home, who were determined to properly clothe him after a rough landing in Alzheimer's Canyon . . .]

"I'm not trying to be difficult. It's just that this thing looks like a plastic diaper," I explain to them.

"You know, hun, that's because it *is* a plastic diaper. I wish I could offer you a selection of pastel colors that would be most attractive on you, but you'll have to wait until we get back to the Home for that."

"Hold it a minute," I say. "I'm not going to any Home tonight. And besides, I've never been to your Shady Home, ever. And I don't plan on starting anytime soon, like . . . ever . . ."

"Aw, baby, that's what they all say. Just give it up now, and come with us, easy."

"You know what? NO!" I'm getting up on my high horse, now. "Think about it—what are they gonna say when you come back with a naked stranger?"

"Geez, Tiffany. The nutball might be half right. What *are* we gonna tell 'em? *I* ain't seen this one before." She's back to talking in a normal voice, just like I wasn't there, or maybe like I'm just too stupid to understand.

Whichever, the gals in white are getting nervous. It's time to play my trump card (no, not *that* Trump!). "You know what? This is a problem alright, but it might be one that could be solved by a clever mind or two."

"Shut yer clam, old man. We wouldn't even have this problem if you weren't here."

"What did you just say, Heather?" Tiffany wants to know.

"I said, 'Shut yer clam, old man!'"

"No, no, *after!*"

"I said we wouldn't have no problem if'n *he* warn't here . . ."

"Heather, you did it!"

"What this time?"

"You solved our effin' problem!!"

"What?"

"Yeah. If there's no geezer, there's no problem."

"Wow," I jump in. "You two are quite something. This really could be the very best time for us to go our separate ways. And no one will be the wiser. Though I must say, it would be close to impossible to beat you two girls in the wisdom department. With no further ado, I'll be on my way. I'd tip my hat if I had one. I suppose I could tip this diaper . . ."

"No! No!! No!!!"

"Just kidding, gals. Whoa, can I take some of those animal crackers and maybe a few juice boxes for the road?"

"Go ahead. Take these graham crackers too . . . Just git. Shoo!! We don't ever want to be seeing you again. Today, tonight, tomorrow, or anytime. And while yer at it, put on your forgetting spell, or whatever you do to get so dumb, and don't be remembering us or the Shady Way Home nor *nothing*!! This is just another day that never happened . . ."

"Have a good evening, ladies."

And I'm gone.

Just as fast as these crinkly Depends will allow me . . .

SKY: **REEVALUATION**

This week, I had my eight-month assessment/reevaluation at the memory center. The usual cast of characters were on hand:

- The efficient and friendly office managers.
- My tester, with her arms full of flash cards, watches, combs, and other professional supplies.
- A random ensemble of white-coated professionals, quietly bustling about, making eye contact with no one.
- The patients, sitting docilely in pairs with their caregivers, waiting their turn to find out what the staff has to share, good news or, more likely, bad.
- And, ruling the roost, Dr. P., patient and unflappable as ever. He also wears white, as befits his station.

After numerous visits here, this place has come to feel familiar and nonthreatening. Jane and I find chairs to wait, but we don't need to wait long. The tester approaches us and whisks me away to her now-familiar office, which, yesterday, also happened to be a portal to the Twilight Zone.

What?!

Twilight Zone? You know, the place where reality and unreality meet? The test itself was not a big deal . . . a number of the words I had to memorize I still remembered from previous versions, which was spooky in itself. Then there was Dr. P., grinning over his computer just like the last time we did this, eight months ago.

"Uh-oh," I say. "Something funny happen?" I offer.

Instead of answering, Dr. P. gently and respectfully guides me and Jane over to our appointed seats at his desk. Now he is asking us the questions. "Did I hear you mention something about cognitive losses?"

"Oh, yeah, I can't remember a single thing any more. I'm always losing track of what I'm trying to say. It's so noticeable!"

"Mr. Yardley, your testing shows otherwise. Your cognitive abilities are showing themselves to be as strong as at any time you have been a patient here."

"Impossible," I blurt out.

Jane just shakes her head and rolls her eyes.

"That is so different from what I see every day," she adds.

Here is how Dr. P. sums it up in his notes:

> Mr. Yardley underwent repeat neuropsychologic testing today. He scored twenty-eight on the Mini-Mental State Exam compared to twenty-seven when tested in February 2018. His score on the ADAS was eight compared to nine in February.
>
> ASSESSMENT: Mr. Yardley remains remarkably stable on formal neuropsychologic testing in spite of both he and his wife indicating that cognition continues to decline.

So, what does this all mean? Are the tests faulty? Hopefully not! They are a key part of a standard assessment meant to screen for cognitive issues that could indicate dementia. If the tests are randomly unreliable, especially to such an extreme extent as Jane and Dr. P. and I experienced, they might lose a lot of their credibility as diagnostic tools.

Here's another idea . . .

A current fad in the dementia community is the importance of keeping your mind sharp: "use it or lose it"; keep your brain tuned. This philosophy can take different forms, but basically focuses on respect and proper care and feeding of the brain so it can be the best brain it can be. Just take a look at any issue of AARP (the over-age-fifty national lobbying group), and you'll see that month's version of exercises to defy aging.

I used to be more skeptical of this kind of thinking, that just changing the fuel mix in our carburetors will turn us into superheroes and keep illness, stress, and troubles far away.

Life is more complicated, I'm sure.

Still, I keep the book my son gave me nearby: *The Mammoth Book of Brain Boosters: Give your brain the ultimate workout every day of the year!*

What helps me the most is keeping myself busy in body and grateful in spirit. Let Alzheimer's take its unpredictable path through my nervous system.

What will be next?

Another dose of (alleged) "remarkably stable" sounds pretty good . . . !?

Mnemo just gives me a wink.

. . . .

SKY: A BIT OF PERSONAL NEUROSCIENCE

It turns out that a new and highly important part of the brain has only been discovered in the last ten years. It's not even its own separate part: It is several structures working together as a hub to help make sense out of the tsunami of information and data. Its name is the default mode network (DMN). Interestingly, this network wakes up and gets to work only when the rest of the body shuts down. So, when the rest of our brains and bodies and minds and consciousness enter downtime, the DMN literally switches on.

The job of the DMN is to keep the lid on, wax the floors when the office is closed, and generally reestablish order. So-called "lower" animals and young children have only undeveloped DMN, if any at all, instead creating a rich world of magical thinking to live in, with layers of wonder. Of course, many adults overshoot as they put together their networks, building DMNs that are over-developed, leading to patterns of self-absorption and rigid thinking.

Michael Pollan, in his hugely popular book *How to Change Your Mind*, invites us along with him as he tours various labs where, for years, scientists have been conducting detailed research into a number of psychedelic drugs. Although the concept of the DMN was unknown for most of these years, the concept quickly came to make a lot of sense to many in the field. Two British scientists posited the idea that one of the effects of the psychedelic drug was to temporarily disconnect the subjects' DMN, opening wide the "doors of perception" (to quote Aldous Huxley), allowing us to experience a reality that is vastly different from our everyday lives, yet at the same time is our reality.

blowing the mind
shaking the snow globe
rebooting the system
tripping

So, once again, what's the point of this brief ramble into and out of neuroscience and psychedelics?

Two things:

1. Coincidence or not, the DMN is one of the first brain structures to be affected in a "typical" run of Alzheimer's.

The other is the hippocampus, involved in laying down, or not laying down, memory. The changes in the brain are apparently not that difficult to find, especially if you have a PET scanner. And a brain at rest.

This scan was the basis of my diagnosis in 2016. At the time, the test was not yet accepted by the insurance industry, but now I see that the PET scan is in contention to be a possibly reliable biomarker, with the potential to identify Alzheimer's disease pre-symptomatically.

2. The other link is more speculative. I know for sure—I can feel it—my hippocampus and other memory-related structures are working overtime just to keep my head above water. Ask anyone who has seen me lately: my short-term memory is the pits.

A Canadian group has recently confirmed that the DMN is one of the very first brain structures "suppressed" by Alzheimer's. I have to wonder if my own DMN is in fact going downhill at the same time.

What brain structures and functions are going along for the ride?

What will it feel like to be on the receiving end of this suppression?

Am I there yet?

. . . .

SKY: BABY

The other day, Jane and I were at the University of Vermont (UVM) as guest speakers for a class on aging and human development. I was tickled to find out that the students' assignment was to read the blog—yes, *this* blog—and create some questions for us.

The class was a seminar, small and intimate, with eight undergraduate students. Perfect conditions for the emotional spillage that was to come. It started when a young woman asked about the picture of the baby with a poem I had written called "Soothing":

> *With my hands, I fashion*
> *my own cradle*
> *For a hurting brain.*

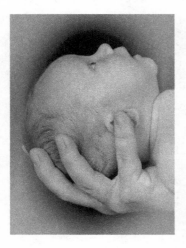

I included the photo simply because it was too powerful *not* to include it. Hands tenderly holding the ridiculously vulnerable newborn, all wrinkly skin and undeveloped brain.

The hands take the very familiar protective position that I find myself in when the world threatens to overwhelm. I can't take my eyes off this baby. There's some meaning here that I'm almost, but not quite, getting. Fortunately, Jane is running the class at this point, so I don't need to worry about my lapse, unless I take too long to return.

And then, suddenly, I get it. And I'm back. I'm mesmerized by this baby because . . . she is *my* baby! Her brain still just partially developed, she is content (for a moment) to turn her gaze fully to mine and soak up her brand-new world through my eyes.

Somehow, we were made for each other, though we are both so new to our worlds . . . vulnerable, open, and not real smart yet.

Wow!! What next?

. . . .

SKY: DOES THIS STRATEGY HAVE A CHANCE?

I've noticed a common thread among many of us living on the dementia continuum. As our short-term memories decline, so do our skills at handling conflict and stress.

Small bumps in the road that we previously would have cruised right through, or maybe not even noticed, now turn into mud pits with danger flags flapping wildly. One of my first signs of neurological trouble occurred early on in the renovation project two years ago, when I happened to overhear two workers talking about their schedules, when they were available for the following week. For some completely unknown reason, I found this conversation threatening, and I made tracks out of there!

As experiences like these accumulated, I began to notice a pattern. I eventually had the opportunity to relearn some key information that had anchored me through decades as a mediator:

> Stress—> Interaction—> More Stress—> Blame Somebody—> More Stress—> More Blame

As long as this pattern remains intact, positive change is impossible. If people in an interaction demand the other side to change first, without acknowledging their own roles, then good luck with that!!

Finding truth in the deeper levels of an interaction is often the route to a happier resolution. I know this to be the case in family and business conflicts. If you're so smart, put it to work with this dementia thing, Sky . . .

What if I choose to interact with the Alzheimer's-modified world that I live in 24-7 with a little more confidence and self-esteem? What might happen then? Looking back, it's safe to say that the times I have lived the most courageously have been the most rewarding.

Why stop now?

What if I took the time to interact with the whole world with care and respect and love, every day? I really mean it; what would my world look like?

I'm on a mission: I want to disable the triggers that would send me into a black hole of anxiety or fear or what-ifs, *and* I want to collect stories of families and people who are bucking the stereotype of Alzheimer's = Armageddon. Even in the smallest of ways.

Now, please don't get me wrong. You will not, never, ever hear me gushing about how happy I am now that Dr. Alz. has become a permanent and forever part of my life. He's slowly and relentlessly pulling out my brain circuits, one by one, until there are no more.

SKY: HOLIDAY 2018

Well, holiday time has rolled around again. One of my personal favorite times of year, celebrating the end of the darkest days and the return of light, if not warmth.

The other day, I took part in a singing ritual, a yearly gathering of friends, old and new, singing our gratitude for the turning of the seasons.

I wondered how things would be different this year. Time passes quickly for me now. This year my friends and I will "celebrate" my entering the third year of my terminal diagnosis. How will my friends react? How will I react?

This party could be an opportunity to catch up.

Sure enough, a friend who I have known since 1973, when we were neighbors in the same tiny Northeast Kingdom town, approaches. In 1974 I gave her some of my favorite blankets when her ancient house on the river burned to the ground on a frigid winter night.

Despite the noise of numerous simultaneous conversations, I recognize my friend immediately as she makes her way across the room.

"Hi," she says with a perky smile. "I'm G."

"Oh, G., of course I remember. You're not exactly forgettable, after all."

As soon as the words are out of my mouth, I know they are wrong. Any memory lapses intruding into my conversation with G. are not about G., but about pieces of my brain that no longer collaborate so well.

But we luck out and end up with a short but warm conversation. Researchers have determined that long-term memories are among the last to fade under the assault of dementia. So our long, even though not particularly deep, history may have helped us.

I haven't exactly been a pillar of cognitive brain power lately. Reading has become hit-or-miss. I have to concentrate hard to keep track of the characters and the plot of the novel I'm working my way through.

In conversation, I'm searching for familiar words all the time. Reading is still worth the extra effort, but I can easily imagine the frustration and agony of when it won't be.

In the meantime, I'll keep trudging along on what my friend J. calls the Journey to the Unknown.

. . . .

SKY AND JANE: THE INCIDENT

Sky:

Well, it finally happened . . . a surprise, intense visit from Dr. Dementor himself. Yes, the Dementor-in-Chief paid me a personal visit just so I don't forget who is in charge.

I shouldn't have been surprised, I suppose, the stage was all set for some chaos:

I was tired, at the end of an exhausting day . . .

. . . maybe even running a fever.

I was far from home—over a thousand miles—doing volunteer work at the Texas-Mexico border.

I was scared.

I was convinced a rowdy Mardi Gras parade would pour around the corner into the New Orleans dive bar where I was holed up with Jane and the baby I was entrusted to keep safe.

I was scared.

I told Jane we had to get out of there. It was no longer a safe place. I heard her try to explain to me that we were not in New Orleans. Dr. Dementor was there. I couldn't see him, just felt his presence in the chaos. The bar was also in the chaos. So was a trampling horde, just out of sight. I knew I could only get out of there by a super effort.

I'm in two places at once. Isn't that impossible? Jane is there trying to talk me down. I can hear her. Beside her is the Doctor, with his heedless trampling street musicians. I know where I have to go. With Jane.

Then, all of a sudden, snap—I'm out . . . back . . . another thousand miles away . . . safe again.

I don't ever want to experience this again, but I know it's just a matter of time.

* * *

Jane:

Sky and I were in San Antonio, Texas, trying to relax after a week of volunteering at a refugee respite center on the U.S.-Mexican border. All the refugees had colds, and we had succumbed the day before, and were challenged by the six-hour drive to San Antonio. Happy to be in a comfy room, we slept, despite our fevers, runny noses, and coughs.

Sky woke early—5:15 a.m.—and insisted we get up and get going.

"I have to do my hearing aids! Where should I sit and clean them? Over there!" He pointed at the room's desk.

"Sky, it's early in the morning. We're not going anywhere for several hours. Go back to sleep."

He went on and on long enough about the hearing aids that I gave up and made us coffee. As he continued to fuss, I logged on to Facebook to pass the time. Friends of ours from New Orleans had been in a pre-Mardi Gras parade the night before, and had posted photos. I showed them to Sky.

Within minutes he stopped raving about the hearing aids and moved on to saying, "I don't want to be in a parade! I don't want to be in a parade!"

"We're not going to be in a parade, Sky. We're not in New Orleans, we're in Texas, we're headed to the ministers' retreat."

"I don't want to be in a parade! I don't want to be in a parade!"

Nothing I said—i.e., giving Sky factual information—helped. He continued to rave about the parade, periodically adding that he was afraid of getting separated from me. I assured him I was right there, and not going anywhere.

Finally, I said I was going back to sleep, and I hoped he would too.

When I woke up, Sky had stopped ranting and raving—about either the parade or the hearing aids. I was relieved. Was he back to normal? What had caused this delirium? A fever? Being in a new place? A new stage of his dementia?

Sky said that he felt like he was "coming back," yet he was surprised to hear that he had been ranting and raving—he knew something wasn't right, but didn't remember what it was. He never told me about the dive bar, the baby, or the street musicians. I just learned about them now, same as you.

Three days later, still not fully "back," he said he wanted to go home, sleep in his own bed, be safe.

So we packed up and hit the road. Five days later we were home.

I often ponder those three hours when Sky entered into a new reality, one that had no relationship to the reality I was in. It still is a mystery to me why it happened, but it gave me a glimpse of what is to come.

. . . .

SKY: HOW'S IT GOIN'?

"Hey, Sky. How's it goin'?"

"You want the long, medium, or short answer? Long and medium: You get the latest hallucination reports. Short: Requires no listening skills, and minimal time commitment."

"Hey, I got time. Lay it on me, man!! Oh, wait, unless it's gonna get disturbing. What do you think?"

"I'll bet you'll be good . . . We can both toss in some of our wicked humor from time to time, keep it light."

"OK, let's rock, then. Full boat, no extra charge for the demented . . . Hey, Sky. How's it goin'?"

"Been better, but thanks for asking. It feels like I'm on the edge of losing both reading and writing in one fell swoop here."

"That's gotta leave a hole, especially for you. I wondered if maybe you've been slowing down a bit on the blog."

"Yep. I've definitely slowed on that and not by choice. The words just aren't showing up like they used to . . ."

So, brain too slow for reading. But definitely not for:
Going out with friends.

Biking next to the lake.

Imagining next summer's garden.

Slipping into the heat of the wood-fired hot tub under the full moon.

Resting by the Earth Clock.

Climbing the cliffs over the lake by Rock Point.

Sharing experiences with others living with dementia.

Family dinner with everything from the garden.

Writing this list of positive things.

Learning new computer skills.

Watching the sun rise over Jay Peak.

Walking over the tumble of ice blocks on the lake.

Looking up to see a huge, noisy vee of northbound Canada geese.

Spraying foam to insulate the new house.

Rigging the Sunfish for her first sail.

Sharing stories with the younger generation.

Watering the newly planted fruit trees.

Watching the fig tree leaf out in the front room.

Hallucinations be damned. I guess I'm doing OK.

. . . .

JANE: EXPECT THE UNEXPECTED

About two months ago, Sky said he felt that he could no longer read books—it was too much work keeping track of the sentences, and he often forgot what he had just read and had to go back to the beginning of the sentence to try again.

Maybe a Kindle would help? Fewer words on a "page," and he could make the font size whatever he wanted. We downloaded some books from the library. That was better than paper books, but still too hard.

He checked an audiobook out from the library. We hauled out our rarely used sound system, and he gave it a try. That was better. With his headphones on, he could sit happily in his chair and "read." I bought him a small, portable CD player so he could listen to books in other locations—in bed, on the porch, at another house. I'm glad we had the money to do this.

Expect the unexpected.

About a month ago, just as the weather was getting better, Sky started taking long bike rides again. Except he found himself having a hard time swinging his leg up over the seat to mount the bike. He found himself falling off his bike if he didn't get a fast-enough start. He started getting too scared to ride his bike anymore, even though he never was physically injured, just psychologically injured.

Today we talked about what to do. Did he want to try a recumbent bike? (Closer to the ground, mounted in a different way.) Did he want to try an adult tricycle? (Sturdy, for sure, but maybe too humiliating? After all, we're in Vermont, not Florida.) Did he want to give up bike riding all together, and take up walking? No clear answers yet, we're still thinking on it. I'm glad we have the money to be able to follow through on a new bike if that's what he chooses.

Expect the unexpected.

A handful of times in the last month, Sky has walked away from a hot pan on the stove when he was preparing his lunch. Once the smoke detector went off. The other times

I noticed and sent him back to the stove. I am waiting, and watching, to see if it's time for Sky to stop cooking for himself. I'd hate for that to happen, but I'd also hate for the house to catch on fire. Good thing the cats know to skedaddle out the cat door when the smoke detector goes off.

Expect the unexpected.

Because of Sky's inability to read books anymore, I recently read aloud Bill McKibben's new book, *Falter: Has the Human Game Begun to Play Itself Out?* We both are concerned with the climate change/climate chaos that is transforming our planet. We both are concerned that the human race may be heading for extinction, that it may be too late to bring this dire situation around. We thoroughly enjoyed the book and have had many deep conversations about what may be ahead for the planet, for the human race, our beloved mountains and lakes, and our family and friends, and how we want to live our lives given this situation. We already live in a net-zero house, and try to keep our footprint as small as we can. And to that we add the philosophy to live each day to the fullest, and not waste time with things that are not important. And, above all—

Expect the unexpected.

JANE: WE ARE WHAT WE DO?

The other day Sky said to me, "I can't do anything anymore." Of course, that isn't true—there are lots of things he can still do. What he meant is, "I can't do many things that I used to be able to do easily and well," like carpentry, gardening, reading, writing, crossword puzzles, board and card games.

We all learn how to do many different things in our lives. I remember vividly learning to read, learning to swim, learning to downhill ski, learning to ride a two-wheeled bike—none of them easy to learn, but oh-so-satisfying once I got the hang of it. My horizons opened up—so many books to read, lakes to swim in, mountains to glide down, and roads to ride. Life was full of endless possibilities.

I can't imagine what it's like to have your world begin to shrink, to have the endless possibilities disappear one by one. I'm watching Sky's world shrink, and while it's painful for me to watch, I know it's more painful for him. So many activities he's enjoyed for so long—gone.

Other people lose the ability to do things they love—it's not just folks with dementia. Accidents or illnesses that cause injury, chronic pain and fatigue, or paralysis take away certain physical abilities. A paraplegic can't run marathons anymore, but they can do so many things with their minds. A blind person can't read books anymore or drive a car, but they can listen to audiobooks, learn braille, and start hiring drivers or take advantage of the good will of friends to get around. More naps help keep up stamina, certain diets help with energy and clarity, technological solutions provide answers. People learn to cope with their new reality and make adjustments.

But for people with dementia, the skills are gone forever, and, in many cases, cannot be substituted for. Sure, audiobooks will work for a while, but the day will come when Sky's comprehension will be gone. Sure, Sky can go into the garden and enjoy looking at the plants, but that's not the same as tending them. Sure, Sky can watch the rest of us do carpentry, and remember when he could too . . . or he can walk away and find something else to do to avoid the pain. Sure, he can still ride his (new, lighter) bike, but the day will come when he won't even be able to do that, and he's wary of being taken out for a ride in a tandem trike pedaled by his son. (I think it's a great idea, don't you?)

For many people, the things that we "do" define us as people: *I'm a lawyer, I'm a doctor, I'm a mechanic, I'm a teacher, I'm a chef, I'm an architect, I'm a bridge player, I'm an athlete, I'm a journalist, I'm a knitter, I'm an artist.* Many people struggle when they retire from paid work—when they lose that particular definition of who they are. They have to remake themselves in a new image, find a new definition, find a new meaning.

But what if you can't "do" anymore? How do you define yourself as a person? How do you find the core of your being? How do you know who you are anymore?

We are so much more than the things that we "do"—take all those "doings" away and what have you got? You've got a person who loves and is loved, who sees and is seen, someone who is unique in all the world—whether or not they "do" anything.

So, Sky, whether or not you can do things anymore is beside the point. You are still you, and you are loved.

(And I want that bike!)

ALZHEIMER'S CANYON
Episode #8

[Having just barely escaped the clutches of two employees of the Shady Way Home, our hero pauses for a look around and to make a plan . . .]

[Thinking out loud] "Yeah, let's get reoriented here. Gotta be careful. I want to see them first, before they see me."

Whoever "they" is . . . or are.

"Ha ha. Lil' feller, you're plumb out of luck on that strategy. Ah'm *always* gonna see you first on account of y'all *never* gonna see me first, or *ever!!*"

"Oh, my goodness, it's Mr. Rhodes! I'm sorry, I completely forgot about you. It's good to see you—I mean, not see you—again."

"Hell, just call me Dusty. And don't bother apologizing about fergettin'. That's just how we roll down here. *Shee-it*, I fergot what I even used to look like, and a long time ago it was too . . . I think."

After a drawled pause, he notes, "Looks like you took my advice about letting go, back there at the San-Di-Flush. I mean, y'all appear to have most of yer original pieces."

"Well, I guess the outfit doesn't leave much to the imagination, does it?" I allow, with a vague glance toward my nether regions.

"Yeah, you right there, pardner," he answers with a wry, invisible grin. "Y'all good now? Traveling kinda light, ah see . . .

"Well, as far as supplies, what you see is what you get"—showing him my meager handful of crackers and juice boxes.

After a longer pause, the invisible cowboy offers sheepishly, "Y'know. I used to get around quite a bit back in the day, and I don't know, but if I kin remember a tinth of what-all I seen, I reckon we could make a time of it, see a few things. You won't be seeing *me*, o' course."

He might be smiling again, but who knows. What is on my mind is that once again it's decision time for me in Alzheimer's Canyon. My record so far is far, far from good. Can I trust this, this spirit-thing, farther than I can throw him? (Which is zero!) I already know that too many of the characters in this bizarre world don't have my best interests at heart.

And I don't want to forget that Dusty saved my life back there at the wall. He didn't have to do that.

And the oily maître d' . . . What role did he take in shooting me through to this Canyon?

And, way, way back at the beginning, that sure looked like Dr. P. calmly waving me in here.

And, and, and, and, and, and, and, and, and, and, and, and, and, and, and, and . . .

My brain, straining at the seams to accommodate every possible argument, is beginning to shut down. What a horrible place to make a decision like this.

In the end, I go with my gut.

"Dusty, is there anyplace nearby where an invisible cowpoke and a newcomer can see the sunset?"

"Buddy, if y'all know how to appreciate a sunset, y'all in the right Canyon. But first we rustle up some vittles and a bedroll. Follow me."

SKY: MY SPIRITUAL LIFE

[Note from Jane: The following are the words that Sky read at the beginning of our workshop, "Nurturing a Dementia Friendly Spiritual Life," which we co-presented (with Linn Possell) at the Dementia Action Alliance conference in Atlanta.]

What I believe . . . a work in progress.

As a species, we human beings have a great capacity to feel and act for good and/or for harm, in close to equal power. This power extends to the capacity to foul our own nests with overpopulation and excess consumerism leading to the extinction of hundreds of thousands of life forms, including our own. The wheels have already been set in motion, mass extinctions have become inevitable—how far will they go?

Remarkably, despite numerous opportunities—and threats—we have so far avoided using nuclear weapons again, our most imminent threat of mass extinction. Continuing to stay alive and love as the technology of war and death ramp up on all sides is cause for celebration.

What we call Nature will continue. Nature doesn't need us to keep doing what she has been doing so successfully for over *4 billion years*: building mountains, eroding them back down, floating continents around over the tectonic plates under them, the whole shebang greased with molten rock and iron.

Whenever I spend time in the familiar landscape of my Vermont home, I am reminded of the power that creates it, and how miniscule my concerns are in comparison. The mountains are always there for me, without complaint, so solid and strong, ready to receive whatever human-based whining I have to offer. The lakes and rivers, too, are there for me, always flowing, moving, creating.

Thank you, rocks and water.

Three years ago, I was hit with a doozy when a PET scan noted problems with my brain's utilization of glucose, its primary nutrient, adding that the scan was also consistent with early signs of Alzheimer's disease.

Bring on the devastation!!

The neurologist's mournful tone and the content of his words combined to feel like nails in a coffin, and my spirit sank like a stone. The doctor assessed my remaining lifespan at six to ten years, offered me Aricept, and had very little else to say as I walked out of the office, stunned.

All I could focus on was the losses big and small, including the loss of my identity, who I was. I didn't know where that could lead except to more losses.

I floated in and out of denial for several months.

Going for long bike rides helped to ground me. There are two bike paths where I live that run along Lake Champlain, and I went there in all kinds of weather when I needed to find peace. There is a beautiful sculpture next to one of the bike paths on the edge of the water—a replica of standing stones—and I would find myself going there. Besides the sculpture, there are vestiges of shipwrecked boats, artistic in their own way. And beyond them, the broad lake with the Adirondack mountains towering over the western shore.

Going there provides me with a sense of mystery, a sense of things being unfinished. Helping me be comfortable with my diagnosis, my dementia, not knowing where this is leading. I can find peace being there, I can lose my terror, I can understand that the world is still unfolding, and so am I.

At the end of that bike path, there is an accessible tree house. I like to climb up—easily since it's accessible to all—and nest myself in this giant oak. It's a very alive place. I have always loved trees, being in the woods, and here I can get a taste of that without leaving town. I respect the woods because the life forms there know what to do, and they always have. Knowing that I, too, am a life form, it takes the pressure off—somewhere, inside, I too know what to do. I too am part of creation and the unfolding of all—wherever we are headed.

My wise niece once told me—everything will work out OK in the end; if it's not OK, it's not the end. That God has better plans for you than you do for yourself. That the Goddess provides. And that you are always embraced by an endless love.

. . . .

SKY: HA HA HA LU SIN AY SHUNS

Jane: I think people would like to know about your hallucinations. I would, anyway.

Sky: Well, it was a big surprise when they came to me. I didn't really know what was going on. And there are different kinds of hallucinations. The simplest kind is when I see something in a rock or a mountain or a cloud and say, "Oh, Look! There's a dog and a puppy playing in the sky!"

The more complicated kind is when they move.

Jane: Move?

Sky: They're very quiet when they move. Sort of like a pet, a cat walking the floor, you see them, but you don't necessarily hear them.

Jane: Do they do anything besides move?

Sky: Oh, that's a good question. With their quietness, they're sort of unpredictable. Like, for example, once I saw some sea lions in the lake—they were swimming around and sitting on rocks—I guess that's not unpredictable except that I know there are no sea lions here in Lake Champlain, in Vermont!

Then there's a whole other category. We have rock sculptures here at the lake, built by Sayer and Emma, and I see those sculptures every single day, many times over the day, and they look different every time. There are emotions going through them.

Jane: What kind of emotions?

Sky: They do a lot of watching without commenting. That way they're sort of a mirror for us, the chance to see something new in the familiar, which is something I like to do anyway.

I saw one the other day, and I knew she was sad.

One of the biggest sculptures—that one there—she has a really wide emotional range. She's one of the more anthropomorphic of the sculptures.

Then, sometimes when I'm riding my bike on the bike path, I'll get the feeling that somebody or something is crowding me or they're approaching from behind, and it gets my attention, but it's annoying, irritating. They're in my space and I don't like it. But . . . they're not there. But they are there. That's a different kind of hallucination—a feeling one rather than a seeing one.

A few times I yell at them before I realize what they are. I don't have names for them yet, but I should. I'm in the habit, if somebody does something dangerous or I don't like it, I yell at them. So I do—I yell at them.

Jane: So sometimes the hallucinations are scary?

Sky: Yeah, especially if they are invisible! Is it a hallucination if it's invisible?

Jane: Are they always invisible?

Sky: Oh, no. Sometimes in the middle of the night, they're so frightening, and very clear. The theme seems to be protecting myself, my home, my family. Someone is always asking for help, yelling even. I can't get dressed and get there fast enough. I can't get there fast enough. It's awful.

Jane: What effect do they have on you at the time?

Sky: At the time, it feels just like real life, and it's really confusing to come out of it. Because—what is reality? What is a dream? What is a hallucination?

For me, hallucinations and dreams, they are there to help me, help me understand more, understand what's going on for me, for you, for the world, it's about health and wholeness (thank you, Jeremy Taylor). I feel appreciative of dreams—and of the hallucinations. I feel like they are something to pay attention to.

Yesterday, there was a group of teenage girls, and they were standing quietly at the edge of the swamp over there and by the time I realized that they were watching me, I realized that it was the same group that had been there recently in the past few days. They were wearing simple brown sackcloth dresses, all the same—but they were allowed to do different things with their hair. They communicated really well without talking.

There's a guy that comes along sometimes, I call him Mr. Green—his whole body, his being is a tree, there are leaves and bark in all the right places. He doesn't have a lot to say, but he's watching. One time I went up to him and reached out and touched him and said hello. He acknowledged that I was there without speaking. That was really cool. I told him I didn't want to encroach on his space, that he knew so much more about this place than I did, and that I hoped we could get along together and talk about things.

Something that's frightening that's popping out now about these creatures, these spirits, is that each one is different. There's not a common language that we all know, but it's OK. But the sad part of the message I am hearing is that communicating may get strange, may get different for me. One of my fears is that communicating will be different, and I don't want that to get in the way of communicating with my loved ones. Everybody has to be part of that and know that and give space to be with each other.

I think for many people, they are really scared of having a hallucination, but you should just give it a chance. I feel appreciative of the work I've done with myself, with others, to deal with all the crap—the fear, the pain, the loss, the inevitability of death—and I think the hallucinations and dreams have helped.

SKY: CAST OF INTERESTING CHARACTERS

I know they're hallucinations. I really do. How else could you explain the Stairway to Heaven? You could describe what it looks like . . .

. . . an elegant sparkling walkway curving graciously up and out of sight into the quiet of the Vermont twilight.

Would it help to describe the people there?

Probably not, since any description would soon veer into the "unreal" with the number of people alone. In the meantime, the Stairway keeps steadily disgorging more people, just like the sidewalks of New York.

I want to tell you about these creatures.

First of all, what are they? They're not human, and they're not not-human. They all look different from each other and from humans, but somehow they're enough human-like that they're endearing. They're small, they're cute, they're watchful and quiet.

Most of them look like the environment that they live in; for instance, some of them look like the leaves that have gathered on the neighbor's rooftop. Some of them have jobs, consistent tasks, like the Fickle Finger of Fate brings along a rig to help him stand on the stump of the tree where he tends to hang out.

They're very solid, I don't have to worry about them, they take care of themselves. One of them, Mr. Green, he brings along his own fun (sort of like cats; they spend time doing stuff we don't know about). He tends to be on the edge of the yard, he's lush and leafy, and sometimes he gets rough and rowdy, and he shakes all over. That's half of him—the other half will back up and run at the other one like they're playing football. They both fall down, then jump up and do it again. It's really funny.

There are a few familiar spots under it, but the Stairway curves up out of sight into the clouds. That was one of the only places I was scared of at first, because there were so many creatures, and they were dressed alike. It was getting to be dark, and I hadn't seen them before, talked with them before. Later I got up the nerve to do that, and I was surprised when I spoke with one, I welcomed her, said I'd like to be friends. My guess is that she was already living there, and I hoped we could all get along now that I had moved in. I think she accepted me.

Now here's a thing that's a little more subtle. The other day, I said to Emma, "Look at that"—it was the echinacea flowers—"I've been seeing creatures today, and I want you to see them." I pointed to the plants, she looked carefully, she shook her head and said, "I just see the flowers." "OK, watch this," I said, and we both backed up. (I had learned that the creatures seem to stress out if you get too close; they don't talk, but look at you, and that's a little bit unnerving.) Then the flowers did something that made me know that they understood me on some level. Normally, they're just flowers growing in the flower bed, but I started to see that they were vibrating and excited. So I took a small step closer, and I could see that one of them, she had a head about the size of a coconut and I could see one eye, but she was there just like all the other ones, quiet, not pushy, and I knew that she would out-wait me in any kind of contest.

Then she directed me to the roof, and there were these large creatures on the roof, at the peak, there were these dudes just showing off, dancing, that sort of thing. I felt like I was safe because there was a lower roof between them and me and the coconut-lady, but they were so graceful to watch. They were strong. They were in green.

I wanted to tell y'all about this because it's so amazing, it's part of my new world, and it all makes sense to me.

. . . .

JANE: MOVING FORWARD BY GOING BACKWARD

Sky said this to me the other day, "I'm moving forward by going backward. When will it be time for diapers?"

I took a breath and said, "We don't need to think about that yet."

How do I respond to a man who needs my help as though he were a toddler? I choose his clothes, help him into his T-shirts, help him with buttons. I cover him up in the middle of the night when he can't figure out which way the quilts go. I help him with technology that he has trouble manipulating. I calm his fears and reassure him in the dark, when he thinks someone is breaking into the house. I read to him since he can no longer read to himself.

But he's not a toddler, he's a man with a lifetime of experience, skills, loves, challenges, rewards. He's a man who still, somehow, has a sharp intellect even though crossword and sudoku puzzles are slipping from his grasp. Yet I read him essays and he understands, digests, and talks to me about what I've just read to him. We can still have amazing conversations, and a few moments later he will hallucinate that the water pipes have burst and water is flooding the house.

His frustration and grief looms large when he can't understand things that he used to easily understand and do—carpentry, machinery, gardening—and he asks me over and over to explain things that I'm doing now—things that used to be his job. It's one loss after another—for both of us.

So we take things one day at a time, one incident at a time, one loss at a time, one precious conversation at a time.

And we move forward by going backward.

. . . .

SKY: AC FALL

[This is Sky's final blog post.]

Here in northern Vermont you ignore the changing of the seasons at your own peril.

Nature always wins. She's the correct team to be on.

Some things you just have to do on time or you may end up miserable, sliding across November ice on the highway.

Other things you just do, well, because they wrestle themselves to a top spot in your neuro-systems at just the right time.

Lately, I haven't been doing so hot with either. It seems I've opened a stress account and a clever system to keep it topped up with automatic payments, only some of which I'm aware of at the time.

Jane is more on top of the big picture . . . but dementia is taking its toll on the whole household. I often have trouble with even the simplest decisions. I have to laugh when I still hear my children, now in their thirties, trying to get a jump on the endless negotiations about what color shirt I'd like to wear, red or blue?

Could this trick from years, years ago really work on me, in present time?

I think maybe so.

I feel like there are so many different ways I'm going downward—I get a lot of enjoyment out of riding my bike, but at the same time I feel like I'm getting weaker rather than stronger and having less balance rather than more balance. I'm at the intersection of what toddlers do when they are learning to walk.

My hallucinations are not really settling down. Sometimes they feel like my friends; other times they keep their distance, and it's annoying and frustrating.

One of my longtime joys—and part of my identity—is exploring the world through books, reading about experiences others have had. But the physical process of reading is now intersecting with my failing brain. I have to work to translate each group of letters into something meaningful, and that's just too hard and too slow. And it is a reminder every day that I'm on the road down. (Thank goodness for audiobooks.)

In the middle of the night I wake up and don't know where I am. I know who I am and who my family is—for now—but I feel like I'm getting a taste of the time when I can't take those paths for granted.

It sometimes takes what feels like a very long time to get reoriented to where I am. *[Note from Jane: Yes, it takes a long time.]* Am I in my house? My neighbor's house? Do I turn on the light? Do I get dressed? I turn to Jane, hold her hand, and let her bring me back to reality.

The world I'm trying to navigate is inconsistent, confusing, hard, and sometimes terrifying. Waking at midnight in a place that I don't know gives me a hint of how my life will be as the disintegration moves ahead.

As Dylan Thomas said: "Rage, rage against the dying of the light."

THE FOURTH YEAR
August 2019–July 2020

ESCALATION.
EXHAUSTION.
LOCKDOWN.

Summer turned into fall. Sky felt exhausted all the time, and we went to see his primary care doc. After testing for multiple possible causes, the doctor said, "It's only your dementia. Your brain is running a marathon every day just trying to keep up. Of course you're exhausted."

Not only was Sky exhausted, he was continually anxious, and his anxiety spilled out all over everything. Keeping up with soothing him—day or night—exhausted me. He was up and down, up and down all night long, and now could no longer find his way to the bathroom. So I guided him there, and back. Helped him into bed the right way, covered him up, and to sleep he would go. Me, I lay awake, finally reading, and perhaps having a wee dram in hopes of sleep.

He lost his ability to ride his bike. His loyal friend C., who had been biking with him nearly every week since his diagnosis, now accompanied him on long walks, which gradually got shorter and shorter as even that skill began to drop away.

He lost his ability to read, relying then on audiobooks. He lost his ability to use the computer, so I had to set up his books, his Zoom calls, his emails. He lost his ability to use his phone, but still carried it "just in case." He lost his ability to write, bereft that he could no longer share his experiences on the blog.

In October, we planned to attend the fall retired ministers' retreat in a nearby state. As I was packing to leave, Sky
said he didn't want to go. Graciously, Sayer agreed to stay
with him so I could go. It was not an easy three days for
Sayer—or Sky. Sky did not remember where I had gone, and
was constantly looking for me, even taking the bed apart in
the middle of the night in his search, sure I was dead. I enjoyed my time with my colleagues, but I knew that was the
last time I would be able to go away.

In early November, we went for our now-annual visit to
the memory center, where Sky was given the same tests and
scored the same as he had every time before. I was stunned.
I asked Dr. P. about the hallucinations.

"Are they scary?" he asked.

"No," I replied.

"Good. Then there is no reason to be concerned about them."

Really?!

We went to the lake with Sayer for Thanksgiving weekend, only to get a call from Emma a few hours later that our
home had been broken into. We packed up in a rush and
drove home in the dark, not knowing what to expect. Sayer
took Sky upstairs to his and Emma's place while I wandered through our trashed house. The contents of nearly
every drawer, shelf, and cupboard had been dumped on the
floor. Anything of value was gone (luckily, we'd taken our
computers with us), and lots of low-value things had disappeared as well. The thieves had cleaned us out. I dealt with
the police, and the insurance company. I found a syringe. I
cleaned up, assessed, reorganized.

Sky's anxiety escalated. He decided he wanted a therapist, and I found someone who specialized in helping people

with dementia. After three visits, Sky said he didn't want to go anymore. He'd wanted to talk with her about death. She wanted him to have a "positive attitude" and talk about all the good things he could still do. He decided that perhaps what he needed was a "social life" and to participate in more "scheduled events." I looked into adult day care, but that didn't seem to be the right thing for Sky. Even though he had dementia, anxiety, and memory loss, his intellect remained strong. I couldn't see him tossing foam balls in a circle, playing with dolls, or doing chair exercises.

I had a major meltdown. My body was covered with itchy hives, I was getting very little sleep, and I had no time to myself since Sky needed help with every little thing from using his audiobooks to getting dressed to using the bathroom and bathing. He no longer knew our house was his home, though he said he was happy to be living there. He complimented us on the good work we'd done to renovate it, though he remembered nothing about that process. In light of all this, Sayer agreed to spend time with him every afternoon, so I could get some rest and some time to myself.

One day, Sky went out for a walk and got lost in the neighborhood. I was starting to worry when the phone rang. It was the receptionist at our dentist's office. Sky had recognized the sign and gone in to ask for help. She graciously called me and waited with him until I arrived to fetch him. That was his last walk alone.

The nights escalated. We had tried several over-the-counter sleeping aids over the years—CBD oil, melatonin, Benadryl—but nothing worked consistently. In desperation, I called Dr. P., who prescribed Risperdal. It only made things worse.

I remembered that our local memory care facility offered a respite service, so I signed up to talk to the staff and have a tour. A person with dementia could stay there for two weeks to two months, whatever time it took to give the family a break. I fantasized about two weeks lying on a tropical beach somewhere, sipping fruity cocktails, reading crime novels, and getting a full night's sleep. I talked to Sky about it. He was willing to check it out, so the two of us went for a tour, lunch, and some activities. He liked it and agreed to go so I could get some rest. We went home and discussed it with Dana and Sayer. Dana was in favor. Sayer worried that we were rushing into a big decision. He sent me to the lake to think it over. He would stay with Sky.

I had a couple of peaceful days at the lake—writing, thinking, walking, sleeping. It was really great. I needed more of that to regain my equilibrium. I returned home and was greeted by an exhausted Sayer. "I never considered that not sleeping would be part of taking care of Sky," he said, and I called the memory care facility to sign up for a two-week respite.

On March 10, 2020, I packed some clothes, a quilt, a few photographs, and a jar of Sky's favorite snack food—pistachios—and drove him to the memory care facility. They greeted him warmly, and he headed off to the activity room. A staff member and I unpacked his belongings, I peeked in to see him engaged in the activity of the morning, and then I headed home, crying tears of relief and sadness. I felt so guilty. I felt like a failure. But I also knew I needed a break. The staff told me it would be easier for me and Sky if I did not contact him during that two-week period. "Enjoy your break," they said. "We'll take care of him for you."

In the meantime, a pandemic was brewing. It didn't seem right to head south to that tropical beach. Maybe I could go to New York City for a couple of days, take in some theater. Nope. Broadway was suddenly shut down. The memory care facility notified me that they were no longer allowing visitors. Emma began working from home. Dana packed up her dog, her cat, her computer, and her clothes and moved to Massachusetts to be with her sweetheart. The governor of Vermont called for a complete lockdown starting March 25. So, on March 24, Sayer, Emma, and I rented a U-Haul and moved lock, stock, and barrel to the lake house. If we were going to be locked down, it seemed like the best place to be. We agreed to leave Sky at the memory care facility for the duration of the pandemic. Little did we know.

The journey into the unknown began. It was unknown for all of us, not just for Sky. Sayer and Emma set up an office and worked at their computers all day. I busied myself with preparing a place for a garden, starting seeds, knitting, reading, wasting time on Facebook, and watching Netflix. I spent a lot of time wondering what was happening with Sky. Was he happy? Did he miss me? When would I see him again? Periodically, he would call me and talk about whatever hallucination he was in at the moment—catching a train to come home, getting the car fixed, traveling in Canada, France, England, New Orleans. He was always on the go. He never asked to come home, or when he would see me again. His voice sounded "normal," and it was so confusing. The social worker would send me chatty emails about any of her encounters with Sky. The doctor called to discuss medications with me—she was trying him on mirtazapine and Seroquel to see if they would calm the hallucinations and help him sleep at night. When I told her about his bad reaction to Risperdal, she wondered if he had Lewy body dementia, and not Alzheimer's.

At the first "care conference" (on Zoom, what else?), the staff said his nights remained "bad," with constant wandering, taking his bed apart, peeing wherever he felt like. He was having trouble using utensils and preferred to eat with his hands. He was throwing his clothes away (and his glasses, I discovered, when they sent me a photo of him and I saw he was wearing someone else's glasses). But they reported that he told them, "Jane and I talked about it, and we decided it was best for me to live here." He began falling on a regular basis, and a nurse would call me to report the latest incident. I missed him terribly, wondered if I would ever see him again, and was eternally grateful that I was sleeping through the night.

We Zoomed with him for his seventieth birthday in April. He was unable to lift his head to look at us, and I wasn't sure he really understood what was going on, but he seemed to enjoy himself. We were all happy to chat with each other. Zoom was still a novelty at that point.

At the end of June, the facility finally allowed in-person visits—outside, masked, six feet apart, for a half hour once a week. Dana and I went together, and it was horrible. I cried through the whole thing, and wondered if I would do it again. But I missed him so much, I knew I would.

Summer again, but different this time. Pandemic. Lockdown. Sky no longer at my side. But I had my garden, and the lake, and the cats, and Sayer, Emma, and Dana. I was no longer exhausted, and I found comfort that Sky had found his people at last.

JANE: LIFE TODAY

"What is this place?"

"How did I get here?"

"Where is everyone?"

You may think this is the beginning of a Talking Heads song, but no, it's just Sky trying to orient himself when he wakes up in the morning. I make coffee and bring it to him, setting it on the bedside table, helping him into his bathrobe, and adjusting the covers as he sits up and wonders.

I ask him questions to help him orient himself to place.

"What do you see on the wall?"

"Are there any cats here?"

"Did you hear an airplane?"

Because we spend time both in our home and at our camp, I ask him these questions to help him remember where we are. Our home has a world map on the bedroom wall, and our cats stay in one place—often on the bed—and, if the wind is right, we're on the takeoff trajectory of the local airport. The first plane leaves at 5:45 a.m. with several more right on its heels. I wonder where they all go? I wonder what all those people are doing? Probably not living with someone with dementia.

I try not to be jealous.

Sky has not been able to be left alone at night for nearly a year now, and we're soon coming on to not being left alone in the daytime. Right now, a couple of hours away in the day is OK, and I relish that time for long walks, doing errands, or having lunch with a friend. I also can rely on Sayer to stay with Sky, or Dana when she comes to visit.

I then have time for bigger pursuits—writing, for example, or some activity related to the nonprofit board I sit on. Now and then I am graced with a few days away, courtesy of Sayer spending the night with Sky and attending to his needs.

Sky's intellect is strong and he—along with so many of the rest of us—is deeply concerned with what is going on in our country, and in our world. But the rest of it? The so-called "activities of daily living" (ADLs) are not so crisp. I continue to choose his clothes, help him dress, remind him to bathe, prepare his food, cover him up at night. And continually orient him to time and place and people. I have to spell the words he wants to put in his crossword puzzle. I have to start and stop the audiobook he's listening to. I write the day's weather and activities on the whiteboard so he can check in with what's going on.

Sky bumped down a few more steps into the rabbit hole after the break-in, not daring to leave the house for several days lest it be broken into again, waking up in the night hearing noises, and fearing the worst.

I spend a lot of time calming him down.

This isn't hard. Not yet. Except for not sleeping through the night when he is afraid and wakes me up worrying about all kinds of things that don't exist. Luckily, Sky naps at least once a day, so I can sleep too. It's just like that advice given to new parents, "Nap when the baby naps." Oh, but I would want to do other things then—like clean the house, read a book, talk on the phone, write in my journal. I know better now, and sleep when he sleeps.

I'm glad all of you are out there in cyber-land. I know

I'm not alone. I don't expect you'll hear directly from Sky again, but we could all be surprised. This is one strange disease.

. . . .

JANE: NIGHTTIME SHENANIGANS

Last night, in the middle of the night, Sky reached over and patted me, then abruptly drew his hand away.

"Oh, I'm sorry," he said. "I thought you were Jane."

"I am Jane."

"Oh, good." And he went back to sleep.

Nighttimes are always an adventure around here these days. And preparing for bed has become a new experience. Sky no longer remembers how to get ready for bed, so I've made him a written checklist:

- Brush teeth
- Pee
- Take melatonin
- Take off clothes
- Get into bed
- Take off glasses
- Put glasses in glasses case
- Put glasses case in bedside stand drawer

I haven't yet had to supervise teeth brushing and peeing, but once those tasks are done, I do have to escort Sky to his side of the bed. He often can't remember where and how to get into bed.

Actually, the "get into bed" activity is much more than that. I have to direct Sky, something like this:

"Sit on the side of the bed."

"Swing your legs up onto the bed." (Sometimes that's in the wrong direction, so I have to be ready.)

"Scoot your butt down." (And I point toward the bottom of the bed.)

When he's far enough to lie down, I no longer tell him to lie "down" because then he continues to scoot his butt down. I've learned to say, "Now lie back."

Once his head hits the pillow, I cover him up, remove his glasses, and stow them safely away (he no longer trusts himself to do this step).

And I hope he goes to sleep—and stays asleep.

I never know.

The melatonin has decreased his nighttime physical agitation and attacking, and some nights he sleeps through the night and wakes up at a reasonable hour.

Then there are the other nights.

Two nights ago, he woke me up at 4 a.m. to tell me we had to go outside and dig up the water line.

"It's still dark. We can't do that now."

"But we have to. The water main is broken. There's a tree down on it."

"Whatever. It's dark. We can't work in the dark." I'm trying to play along.

"But we have to!" he insists. "Check all the faucets!"

I get up, turn on all the faucets. The sound of running water does not seem to soothe him.

"The water is fine."

"No, we have to fix the water line."

I try something new.

"We're in a city. Public Works will take care of it."

"We're in a city?"

"Yup."

And on and on we went. Sky got more and more agitated about the "broken" water line, and despite me holding him, speaking to him soothingly, either playing along or giving him facts, nothing worked. I gave up.

"How about some coffee?" I asked.

"That sounds great!" said Sky, and at 4:30 a.m. we were up for the day. Coffee in hand, lights on, and me reading from the online *New York Times* finally soothed him. Even though the story was about Iran and our almost-war.

He had his first nap at 8:45. Mine was at 11.

Expect the unexpected.

. . . .

JANE: GOING, GOING . . .

"I don't know how to get to the co-op."

Sky was home after about ten minutes instead of the usual forty-five minutes that it takes to walk to the co-op, grocery shop, and walk home. He had headed out to buy supplies for our recently inaugurated Burger Night, when we have dinner with Sayer and Emma and other friends who come by. We buy the food, and Sayer does the cooking. It's always yummy, and something to look forward to. But no more shopping for Sky.

"Is that someone I should meet?"

Sky was coming in the front door, while Emma was coming in the back door. He beckoned me over, and said the above while pointing at Emma. Emma, Sayer, and I were startled, but I calmly replied, "That's Emma." We all wonder when it will happen again.

"Jekyll Place."

For almost four years, we have been living here on Hyde Street. We—Sayer, Emma, Sky, and I—bought the house, renovated it, and have been happily calling this place home. We have a great backyard loaded with garden beds and fruit bushes. We live within walking distance of downtown. We have fine neighbors, by and large, and, except for our recent break-in, it's been a peaceful place to live. Sky doesn't remember that it's called Hyde Street anymore, but he's come up with the next best.

"We need to make plans. Where are we going to sleep tonight?"

Not only does Sky not remember the name of our street anymore, he no longer knows this is our home. Every morning and every evening, he wants to know where we are going to sleep. Despite me telling him this is our home, and showing him our bed with the quilts I made for us, he repeats the question multiple times a day. At other times, he thinks we're just starting the renovations or are building another house on top of this one, or maybe another one in the backyard. We've been having this conversation every day, multiple times a day, for the past two weeks.

"You've just heard some very important information. Let's take a few moments right now to consider this material, and then we'll open it up for questions."

I usually have a book that I'm reading out loud to Sky, as he can't read the printed word anymore and relies on audio-books. When I find something interesting that I think he'll also enjoy, I plan on spending some time every day reading to him. So, the other day I started reading *On Tyranny* by Timothy Snyder (excellent book!), and when I finished the first chapter, Sky said the above to some mysterious class across the room. Not only did he say this, he said it in a very professorial voice, a voice I have never heard come out of his mouth in all these thirty-five years we've been together. I imagine he was channeling one of his Amherst professors.

"That's M. She had a sewing business."

As the definition of "short-term memory loss" now includes almost everything going back four years, Sky's long-term memory is excellent. He lived on a commune for fifteen years in the 1970s and '80s, and one of his co-communards has been posting photos on Facebook of the good old days of the back-to-the-land hippies. The poster will ask, "Does anyone know who these people are?" and Sky will always have an answer. Not only will he know their name, but he'll also be able to tell you something about them, how long they stayed, how they contributed, etc.

The brain is a mysterious thing.

ALZHEIMER'S CANYON
Episode #9

[Our hardy traveler has decided to cast his lot with the invisible cowboy, but first a trip to the store . . .]

"Hey, Dusty, I don't know where we're going, but I would *really* appreciate getting out of this plastic monstrosity," I let him know. "As you know too well, I got nothing. *Nuttin' left* after that trip through the San-Di-Flush!!"

"Sure, buddy! What do you want? Brooks Brothers? L.L.Bean? Salvation Army?"

"I don't think you're getting it yet, Dusty. A few hours ago I had my car, three credit cards, $450 in cash, and an E-ZPass. Now, look at me, all of it gone!"

"If you don't mind, pardner, I'd rather not look too close right now," he answers, with a sidelong glance at my crinkly dipes. "We'll get you back in high cotton in no time. And, as for money, y'all won't be seeing that stuff no more."

"But, but, but . . ." I mutter.

"Why you newbies all the same? Scared o' your own shadows all the time?

"You got a lot to learn, my friend, but I have confidence in you. I think you got a good attitude. Keep you on the up and up side of things," he smiles. "Or, at least *look* that way," he adds with a grin.

"C'mon buddy, we got work to do before the sun goes down."

It's only now that I begin to focus on where we are, trudging slightly downhill on a gravelly road. There are patches of grass here and there that I jump to like a frog on lily pads. Spectacular cliffs loom up on all sides. My palms sweat when I think back to earlier today, all alone traversing cliffs like those, just hoping to stay alive.

No other people in sight, so perhaps I have escaped the clutches of the Shady Way Home. Temporarily, at least. The road twists like crazy, though, so I can't see much, either forward or back, besides the massive rock formations.

Suddenly, a familiar voice: "Not far now, good buddy."

Damn. It's so easy to forget that guy. You think being invisible might have anything to do with it? Then again, I also just forgot what I'm doing on this godforsaken footpath. OK, OK, now it comes back, I got it, I got it! Me and Dusty on a shopping trip. I got it! And around the next bend is a mini shopping center or whatever you'd call a strip mall scaled down to a dirt crossroads out in the boonies with no one around.

"Welcome to Pilgrim Village. Course, nobody around here calls it that. They mostly just call it Pill-Ville, on account of it's the biggest drugstore in three days' walk. Oh, heavens, you must've lost all your meds on that cliff too. What can I get for you? Start with an economy bucket of Aricept maybe? Or are you up to Memantine? If I remember right, Pill-Ville had a good sale on those two not long ago."

"Dusty, I don't want to disappoint you, but I don't take any meds. Oh, wait! Will the Pill-Ville have any Band-Aids? I think my feet will appreciate them tomorrow, after this hike. I'm pretty beat right now, if I think about it."

"OK, bud. How's if I go down to the Pill and pick up what we need. Y'all stay up here—better, stay behind that big rock there, and I'll meet you back up here. I haven't forgotten that sunset. Fifteen-twenty-minute walk, and we'll be there. Curl up and git some shuteye if y'all want. I'll be back in a flash . . . Joke, son. Heh, heh."

Lord, Lord, what a day! I want to follow Dusty's progress down to the Pill, until I remember there's nothing to see. And he was warning me about staying out of sight behind the boulder, right? His suggestion of a nap makes more and more sense as the minutes drag away. Maybe I'll just rest my eyes . . .

JANE: **RESPITE IN THE AGE OF CORONAVIRUS**

While in respite, Sky calls me several times a day, and we chat for a long time or a brief minute or two. He has all kinds of things to tell me, none of which are based in reality. I listen and then go on to tell him about my day. I try and tell him about the coronavirus, how I'm not allowed to visit him, how schools and restaurants and many businesses are closed, but I'm not sure how much sinks in. Today he told me our neighbor (the infamous Mr. L.) was responsible for the virus, and that the military had arrived at the facility and he was worried they would damage his car. He also told me he has a suitor, but "didn't want to go into detail over the phone."

Given the unknown nature of the virus, and how long this crisis will last, my family and I have decided it is best for everyone for Sky to stay in the memory care facility until it is all over. He will be safe, and cared for by competent, well-trained staff. He will have interesting activities and great meals, and people to talk with him 24-7.

In the meantime, I have started seeds—the gardening season will soon be upon us, with new life, and new hope. The ice will melt in the lake, the fruit trees will bud out, and life will go on as it does.

My best to all of you as you traverse this unknown time. May you be safe. May you be loved.

JANE: RESPITE IN THE AGE OF CORONAVIRUS 2

The world has changed since I posted last. And so has my life. And so has Sky's life.

I am looking out onto beautiful Lake Champlain, having left our home in Burlington for our camp in northern Vermont, on the Canadian border. If we're going to be on lockdown, what better place to be than out in the country, with a view of the mountains and the lake, on a road that crosses into Canada and therefore has very little traffic, given that the border is now closed to all but commercial traffic. It's quiet and peaceful—maybe too quiet and peaceful.

But the cats like it, and we're grateful that we have this option. I'm here with Sayer and Emma, our co-tenants in our house in Burlington. Since they're both working from home, we can't see Sky, and we have no idea how long this will last, it seemed like the right move. We rented a U-Haul, brought up extra furniture, bikes, computers, all the food and alcohol we had in both houses, lots of books, games, art supplies, yarn, fabric, and sewing machines. (And the cats—who, we discovered, are not fans of traveling.) We found a friend to live in the Burlington house and watch over it.

All was settled. We just had to wait for the virus to play itself out.

Then I got a phone call from the facility. Sky had a fever and wasn't feeling well. They tested him for the virus, and we had a tense and scary thirty-six hours until the test came back negative. Both we and the staff at the facility breathed sighs of relief. (The majority of Vermont cases are in nursing homes or other senior living facilities.)

But all is not well with Sky. I had a "care conference" yesterday with several staff members from the facility and got a lot more details about his life there (given that our brief phone calls are only about his hallucinations, I really had no idea what was going on for him).

He remains mainly lost in the world of his hallucinations, some benign, some not. His nights are particularly challenging, as he wanders and doesn't always find the bathroom—at least not his own bathroom. He has taken to dismantling the furniture in his room, and he apparently is fond of throwing things out—including his glasses, his toothpaste, and some of his clothes. They have not found the right combination of medications to soothe the hallucinations enough to allow him to sleep. He has started to need help—"cueing," they call it—using utensils to eat his meals.

I don't think we'll be bringing him home.

But at least he's no longer asking me to bring him home. In one lucid moment last week he said to me, "I like it here. There are other people like me to hang out with."

It's an unknown time for all of us. I'm trying to learn to live in the moment, to be grateful for what I do have, and to accept that I cannot see Sky, for who knows how long. I'm trying to trust that the staff are doing their best to care for him and keep him safe.

JANE: UNCERTAINTY IN THE AGE OF CORONAVIRUS

My last two blog posts were about "Respite in the Age of Coronavirus." However, Sky is no longer on respite at the memory care center, but is now a permanent resident. Given that the world is still topsy-turvy, it seemed the best thing to do. So, I signed all the papers and wrote an even bigger check, and there he stays.

It's lonely without him, and it's also peaceful. I sleep through the night every night now, unless I am woken up by a cat doing some kind of cat thing, like throwing up, meowing at me, or getting into a fight. Luckily, Sayer and Emma were still up the night the raccoon tried to come in through the cat door, so I happily slept through that event. Sleep is a wonderful thing.

But here I am, in this beautiful place where it is finally summer and the garden is thriving, though I have to water every day—no rain for ten days. I spend several hours a day tending the vegetable garden and the fruit trees and bushes that we planted in the past couple of years. For the past two summers, Sky tended the orchard—watering, weeding, mulching, mowing. He loved hanging out with the trees. Now it's my turn.

For thirty-five years, Sky and I gardened and tended fruit trees and bushes together. It was one of the things that drew us together: Our love of the natural world and of growing our own food. We complemented each other—he liked preparing the soil, I liked planting. He liked weeding and harvesting, I liked canning and freezing. We both would put the garden to bed for the winter, and then enjoy relaxing indoors with our kids, warmed by a woodstove fueled by wood we had cut, split, and stacked together. We were a team.

I miss being part of a team. A partnership.

Sky and I continue to talk on the phone once or twice a week. I let him call me, hoping that he'll be more lucid than when I call him. But no. He lives in his hallucinatory world 24-7, and I never know what he will say. During one call, he told me he was so excited that I'd just had a baby named Califa. During the next call, he told me he was at the train station waiting to board the train to come home, but he had to wait while they backed up the train. We chatted briefly, and then he told me the conductor called "All Aboard!" and he had to go, but would be home soon. Yesterday he told me that there were two Black people next to the phone booth; they were two or three inches tall and they were kissing each other.

I never know what he will say. I listen and make appropriate comments. I am grateful that he still knows who I am, and I am sad that we can't have a real conversation anymore. That was something else I loved about being with Sky—we've had years of interesting conversations.

But he did say something else yesterday that was pure Sky, and I think wise words for all of us at this uncertain time:

"It's foolish to try and control everything. It just makes for more heartache and more pain."

Right on, Sky.

JANE: **THE VISIT**

Ten days ago, the governor of Vermont lifted the restrictions on visits to residents of elder care facilities. The state department of health issued guidelines for visits and, based on that, Sky's facility issued their own—outdoors only, six-foot distance, everyone in masks, and the visitors were questioned about possible symptoms of the virus and had their temperature taken. Visits must be scheduled, only two visitors per resident, only one visit per week, maximum forty-five minutes. No exchange of gifts, obviously no touching.

I wasn't sure I wanted to visit Sky. I was concerned that it would upset him—seeing me and then having me leave him instead of bringing him home. That he would be agitated afterward. That he wouldn't understand the masks and the no touching. That it would just be too hard on him.

I decided to wait and get a report from the facility as to how other residents were handling these strange new visits.

The report came a few days ago—people were enjoying them, and there didn't seem to be any fallout.

OK. I decided to give it a chance, especially because our daughter Dana said she wanted to come too. She thought it would be fun to sing with Sky—something the two of them had loved doing together over the years. She figured singing would help, since Sky seems to not be able to have a conversation anymore.

I made the appointment, and Dana and I arrived the prescribed ten minutes early to be screened. We were ushered into the courtyard of the facility, where three visiting stations were set up with chairs marked six feet apart, labeled for the resident and the visitors. The other two stations were occupied by visitors and residents. We were offered water, and Dana was allowed to bring her dog along. We waited for Sky.

And there he was, shuffling along, being held by the nurse to steady him. His head hung low, eyes facing the ground. He had a Band-Aid on his forehead—he's been falling with increasing frequency these days. The nurse had to assist him to sit in the chair, and then she left.

Dana and I said hi. No response. I asked Sky to lift his head so he could see us. He tried briefly, gaining maybe a half inch, and then he got agitated. "I can't. Don't make me." I said fine, just relax.

And then he launched into what can only be described as a Sky-monologue, a lecture even, talking about a variety of things that were happening in his current reality. A lot about energy—good energy, bad energy, people stealing energy, people giving energy. As he escalated through this topic, I wished I had a way to record what he was saying, as much of it was really interesting and I would have liked to listen to it again. I should have brought paper and pen to take notes.

After energy, he wandered into other topics—lakes, outhouses, nature, and the protest march at which he was killed. Dana and I asked him questions: What was the protest about? Where did the protest take place? What lake are you talking about? Tell me about the outhouse that was made out of a car. Sometimes he could answer us, and sometimes he couldn't. As the visit wound down, Dana sang him a James Taylor song. He had no reaction. I had thought he would sing along—he still sings (so the staff tells me), and he still knows all the song lyrics. That's something he's always done—he has a song for every occasion—so I was surprised that he didn't really respond to Dana's song.

I cried through most of the visit.

When the visit was over, the nurse came to retrieve him. No goodbye from him, no acknowledgement that we were even there. He struggled to get out of the chair and start to walk. The nurse was patient with him as she guided him along the path. And then he was gone.

But one thing he said has stuck with me: "I want to be sure to get the most out of this experience."

Once again, pure Sky. I hope he's getting what he wants.

THE FIFTH AND FINAL YEAR
August 2020–February 2021

THE END IS
A BEGINNING

The pandemic eased in the summer of 2020, enough that we hoped it would soon be over. I tended the garden, went swimming and kayaking, and decided to sell our half of the Burlington duplex to Emma. As much as I had liked living in town, being on the lake was more peaceful, and certainly more beautiful. I was sad that Sky couldn't spend the summer with me—or at least have a Sunday afternoon visit—since he loved being on the water so much, but I knew it was too far, and would be too disruptive. And besides, Sky had grown fearful of being in the car long before he went to live at the memory care facility, so I knew a visit to the lake would not bring him joy.

I had to content myself with continued outside, masked, no-touch visits once a week or so, but was never sure that either Sky or I enjoyed them. Was it enough just being able to lay eyes on him, even if he was drooling, unable to lift his head to look at me, and unable to get in and out of the chair without help?

But at nearly every visit he said something so profound, so Sky, that it made all the visits worthwhile:

"I haven't done enough with my life, and time is running out."

"We have to be ready for change."

"Being alive and showing up—that's the most important thing."

"That song ["1000 Beautiful Things," sung by John Boutte] gets you in the gut every time."

"I love you. We're just going to keep figuring things out, right?"

At one visit, the nurse who was helping him get situated asked us how we met. I told the story of the restaurant owner and the produce man and added, "It was a great romance." Sky lifted his head, looked at me, and said, "'*Was*'?!" and smiled. He knew me for sure. That made me so happy!

At the end of August came the clincher: "I have a one-way ticket out of here, and it runs out in March or April." Was that when he would die?

Summer turned to fall, and I was busy with the garden, with food preservation, with moving all of our things out of our Burlington house in preparation for the closing. No longer needing to furnish two houses, I took two loads of stuff to the Goodwill, sold or gave away a bunch of furniture, and brought what was left to the lake.

In October, Sayer and Emma moved back to Burlington, and I was alone with our two cats, Tubby and Pogo. I hadn't lived alone for thirty-five years. It took some getting used to, especially learning how to cook for one. I had my last in-person visit with Sky mid-October. The pandemic was escalating, and in-person visits (even six feet apart) were cancelled. It would be phone calls or Zoom from here on out.

At the end of November, my brother died. He had lived a year longer than the doctors predicted, and was quite pleased with himself. He had made it to eighty, and six months beyond. But, because of the pandemic, the hospice house where he spent his last two days only allowed two visitors. His wife and son were with him until the end, but I was not allowed to say goodbye.

Zoom calls were challenging for Sky. He generally needed a staff member to help him, to position the device so that he could see me, to keep him on task. Often we just sat and said very little. "I just want to look at you," he often said, or, "Thank you for loving me." Other times, he was too "busy"—hiking, mooring boats, repairing cars. It was bittersweet. I was so sad not to be able to be in the same room with him, touch him, hang out with him, and really see what his life was like. The Zooms became more frustrating and less fun. I asked the staff just to have him call me if he wanted to talk. On the rare occasions that he did, it seemed that he could no longer finish a thought, and it didn't even frustrate him.

I began to get more and more calls from the nurses, saying he had fallen or injured himself somehow. Some of the nurses would want to chat with me, tell me how much they loved Sky, and share a story about his latest antics. I knew they meant well, but it made me so sad to be missing out on all of it. The doctor called and said she was going to order some physical therapy to see if that would help with his strength and balance. The physical therapist called to report that the PT didn't seem to be doing anything, but she was going to keep at it.

Then, in mid-February, the doctor called to say that when Sky woke up that morning, he was unable to bear weight and he screamed in pain. She feared a broken hip or pelvis. X-rays showed no break, but blessing upon blessing,

I was allowed a "compassionate care visit." I found Sky unresponsive, sitting in a wheelchair. I was just so happy to be at his side, to touch him, to kiss him, to hold his hand. He "came to" a few hours later and recognized me. Then he drifted away again.

His decline was rapid. I was allowed to be with him 24-7. Finally, finally, finally, I was able to be with him, to touch him whenever I wanted to, to see what life was like at the facility, to hear the stories the staff told me about Sky.

I tried to sing to him, but it made me cry.

Dana, Sayer, and Emma visited. Sky's sisters spoke to him on the phone. He was mostly unresponsive, but one afternoon was awake briefly, enough to tell me I was beautiful and to sing some songs with Dana.

On February 23, 2021, one week after not being able to walk, Sky took his last breath.

JANE: MUSINGS

I've been rereading my mother's journals. She started them five weeks after my father died in 1994. It seems as though she wanted someone/something to talk to. My father was quite sick the last eight years of his life, which put a dent into the busy social and travel life they'd had over their years together. This frustrated my mother immensely. She was not a good caregiver, and seemed to resent my father's decline. She gradually had to be in charge of all aspects of their life—no longer did my father make the travel reservations, get the oil changed in the car, or host the cocktail parties. Fortunately, she was a competent woman who was not afraid to take on the extra responsibilities beyond her life as a mother and a homemaker, but she clearly wished things could be otherwise.

Her journals mostly chronicled who she went out to eat with, where, and what foods she indulged in, activities of her children and grandchildren, and her concerns about her own health. And a whole lot about how lonely she was, and how much she missed the "good times" with my father. She was a very social person, so perhaps living alone after all those years—fifty-four—was just too much of a shock.

I think about her loneliness because I don't feel lonely without Sky. I feel sad, certainly. I feel relieved that I no longer have to care for him 24-7. I find peace in knowing that I can come and go as I please, I can eat or sleep when I want to, and stay up late watching too much Netflix.

But I do miss our easy companionship. I miss talking with him—we used to talk about everything from current events to what to plant in the garden to personal feelings to our careers to our children to where we were going to travel next. Everything under the sun. Now when I visit him he doesn't talk *with* me, he talks *at* me, and he talks less and less all the time. He is having a hard time finishing his sentences, even his hallucinatory ones. The subject changes from one sentence to the next. I take notes, hoping to find some meaning in what he says, but I generally don't find it.

He also doesn't respond to what I say either. I tell him about the garden, or something our kids or our cats have done, and there's just a blank look on his face. The next thing that comes out of his mouth has nothing to do with what I just said. So I mostly don't talk anymore; I listen, and I hope, and I just look at him and wonder what it's like to be him.

I've decided to take a break from visiting. I don't think Sky is getting anything out of it—on the contrary, I think the visits bother him. The last few times he has asked to go back inside long before our half hour was up. I've made a plan with the social worker, and when she sees him, she's going to ask him if he'd like to talk with me, and if he does, she'll set up a phone call. We'll see how it goes. Cooler weather is changing the nature of the outside visits anyway, so this may be for the best.

So I keep living my life, wondering how the pandemic will play out, how the election will play out, how the climate crisis will play out, and whether I'll have enough canning jars and lids to deal with the garden's abundance. My thoughts always turn to Sky, off and on throughout the day. I keep on taking things one day at a time.

ALZHEIMER'S CANYON
Episode #10

[Our unnamed hero is resting his battered body in the shade of one of the countless billions of boulders in Alzheimer's Canyon. He is anxiously and sleepily awaiting the return of Dusty Rhodes, his invisible benefactor, who is shopping at Pill-Ville. Don't forget: His entry to the Canyon has literally stripped him of everything he owns, including the shirt off his back and the pants off his butt. All that remains is what he has been able to cobble together: A somewhat beat set of adult diapers, now rapidly nearing the end of their useful life . . .]

Now, when did he say he'd be back? Fifteen minutes? Or was it fifteen minutes walking to the sunset place? And, wait a minute, forget about sunset . . . That's the full moonlight bouncing off the rock towers providing the light anyway. What the fuck is going on around this place, and . . . when?

"Talking to yourself again, good buddy? Careful, now, keep that up and you could wind up with a personal Zoloft prescription. Ask me how I know."

"Dusty, so glad to see you!—of course, I mean, *not* see you—again!"

Looking around, I see no stuff. "Uh-oh, problems in Pill-Ville, Dusty?"

"What, you doubt my skills, pardner?"

"Well, no. It's just that I don't see your stuff . . ."

"Of course y'all don't see my stuff. And why? Why don't y'all see my stuff? There's a very simple answer, knucklehead . . . Y'all don't see my stuff *because it's my stuff*! Now keep standing right there and watch this. I'll show you something. Y'all might want to use your ears too. Now, hush!"

I hush.

"What do you hear?"

"Just the same plastic diaper crinkling I've been hearing all day."

"You quiet y'all's self, listen closer, and tell me what y'all hear," says Dusty.

It's really quiet out there. I strain to hear something, anything beyond my breathing and a distant breeze. Wait, what was that? A faint repetitive noise somewhere overhead.

"There's something tapping up over our heads, Dusty."

"That so, bud?"

"Yeah, Dusty, something different."

"Jes' stay still now. Sit and pay attention."

I sit. I stay. I pay attention. I hear my breathing. I maybe hear Dusty's too (?), and, so very lightly, tap, tap, tap . . .

All of a sudden, a crash, and off my face bounces a plastic-wrapped pair of Fruit of the Loom briefs, size M.

"Dusty, what the hell?"

"I got you a few pair, want to try it again?"

"Yessir!"

"White all right?"

"How do you do that, Mr. Dusty?"

"Easy as falling off a rock . . . Jes' look close and pay attention. See those undies on that ledge?"

"Sure, but . . ."

"Keep watching 'em."

All of a sudden the package is gone, vanished.

"Dusty!"

"You want 'em back, bud?"

"Sure, but . . ."

"OK, last one for now. I know it's getting kind of dark, but looky here for a *very* special Fruit of the Loom." And all at once, a package of underwear flies straight upward at high speed, reaches its apex, then returns toward Earth. At about five feet from the ground, the package vanishes with a snap.

"Hey, Dusty, thanks, man."

"Actchally, we ain't done yet, buddy. That is, unless y'all's one o' them *nood*-ists, ah figured on a few basic clothes to get you by. Plus, we all got to eat, right?" Dusty takes a few steps back, revealing camping supplies, food, and a few layers of comfortable clothes.

"Holy mandoli! This is amazing, Dusty. Wow! It's like you touch something and it disappears?! For real?!" I quickly start pulling on clothes before they disappear again.

"Disappearing is a little strong. More lahk losin' its visibility for a while. But we ain't gonna talk more about this now. Y'all got to learn the basics first. And there's a whole lot o' basics. And you got a whole lot to learn. C'mon, let's repack this while we're talkin', so we can get to the viewpoint."

I am wired. I just can't believe what might be possible down here. I've got to make a few calls . . .

"Dusty! I forgot to remind you, but my phone got trashed when I let go of the cliff back there."

"No fergettin' involved, bud. I was there. I saw the whole thing. Y'all's dead lucky to be here, kickin' and grinnin'. And, nope, no phone service in the Canyon. No need for any of that techno-stuff anymore. Here, follow me up this trail. It's just a bitty ways."

* * *

[An hour, more or less, later. The boys are stretched out on their sleeping bags, quiet but for the tumult of stars . . . so many stars. Their campfire is burning low, random embers crackling.]

"Dusty, why is this vista place called Sunrise/Sunset?"

"Wahl, finally an easy question, thank you. You know how out on big water there's floating, colored buoys to guide you? Well, you won't find them out here. Too much to remember, really. 'Red, Right, Returning.' Too much to forget. We don't name hardly nuffin' out here. What's the point? There's one direction we all end up with . . . Down.

"Maps and charts are good for headaches, mainly. We try to reserve naming for simple things that have some meaning on their own. Take this place. You could probably answer your own question about the name. You have skills. I can tell. Try. Why would a place be named Sunrise/Sunset?"

"Umm, because it's especially interesting at those times?"

"Bingo, pardner."

[The silence settles deeper over the camp.]

"And one more thing. We don't have a name for you yet."

"We?"

"For the Canyon. For your new self."

"You're not gonna get cult-y on me now, are you, Dusty? I'm just me."

"Sure, you're just you. You'll always have that you inside somewhere. And, you will *never* be that person again. You on a one-way street, brother. And I got y'all's name, too."

Invisible Dusty was twinkling now.

"Like I said, I like your attitude, bud. We can call you Explorer . . . X for short. Yeah, I like that fine . . . X."

JANE: **CHANGE OF SEASONS**

It's blustery and raining today with temperatures dropping from the sixties to the forties. Prediction is that it will be forties from here on out. No more warm weather reprieves like yesterday, when it was in the seventies. Time to turn inward, and stay inside. There are still some holdouts in the garden—carrots, cabbage, kale, spinach, parsley, peas—but everything else has died and been pulled to be added to the compost pile. Life and death.

I visited Sky yesterday after a month's absence. There were only two phone calls in that time, brief calls, where Sky wanted to tell me what he was doing ("Just finished tiling the bathroom! It looks great!"; "I've been baking bread with the kitchen ladies and just bought a new grill."), and then, abruptly, he says he has to go. All I can do is listen to his voice—which sounds completely "normal"—so I am confused for a moment. Maybe he doesn't have dementia? Wait, no. He does. And then he is gone.

The staff calls me every time he "falls" (or places himself on the floor), which is happening with greater frequency. They're not really falls though—he's just busy doing different things, like a "project" that involved him crawling across the floor, or sleeping on the floor in someone else's room. I still wonder what it's like to be him.

Yesterday he hardly spoke, mainly looked at the floor, and muttered from time to time. He said Gary Oldman and Sean Connery were there. He kept repeating the words for ice cream (*morozhenoye*) and please (*pozhaluysta*) in Russian. He said, "There is good potential if I have enough energy to follow them." Though when I asked what he meant, he did not respond, just like he did not respond when I told him about the nice weather, or about a friend who had died, or that we took the boats in for the winter.

Once again, I am faced with the decision of whether or not to keep visiting him. It is painful for me, but I think it would be painful to not see him. So much pain all around.

The changing seasons also mark the time of year when we remember our dead. There has been a lot of death recently among my friends and their loved ones. Cancer, in particular, is taking too many people too soon. We honor their lives by remembering them, the gifts they brought to the world, the challenges they faced. We look our own mortality in the eye. And then we go inward to await spring's rebirth.

Between the virus and the election, there is a lot of stress and anxiety out there—and in here. I grieve the end of the garden season, the lake season, the boating season. I grieve the loss of friends and colleagues. I grieve the loss of the Sky I've known and loved for 35-plus years.

Thanks for sharing in our journey.

. . . .

JANE: THANKFUL

I sit here at my desk looking out on yet another gray November day. The clouds hang heavy, there are scattered rain showers, and the lake, for once, is calm. Before too long I'll go out for a walk, warm enough to be pleasant. Yesterday I was also sitting here at my desk, and I watched a fog bank roll in just as the sun was setting—peeking out behind clouds only to disappear. That's November for you.

It's quiet. Just like it was yesterday, and the day before, and the day before that. I live alone now, the first time in thirty-five years. The only sounds I hear (when I'm not watching Netflix or listening to music) are a periodic cat meow, squeak, or purr, birds chirping at the feeder, an occasional passing vehicle, and the wind in the trees. I am as close as I can be to the natural world without actually being outside. I miss being outside. I miss working in the garden, swimming, kayaking, and having the windows open all the time. But I am very thankful for my strong, secure, and warm house.

Yesterday when the fog bank rolled in, I was having a Zoom call with Sky. With the escalating cases of COVID here in Vermont, we're back on lockdown, and Sky's facility canceled all in-person visits. This was our second Zoom visit, and how much better they are than in-person visits! What a gift that I don't have to decide whether or not to make the trek to struggle with yet another uncomfortable, painful, and frustrating in-person visit. On Zoom, Sky can actually see me, and I him. He's in the secure space of his own room, door closed, quiet and peaceful. A staff member is with him, to handle the technology and answer any questions. Sky can end the call whenever he wants to. I can see his room. It feels much less stressful for both of us.

He didn't say much yesterday. He didn't realize/remember that it was Thanksgiving, despite having just had the big holiday meal with the other residents. Sky was never a big Thanksgiving fan, though he always liked to eat what was served. Then, when I was the minister in Derby Line, he decided the best way to celebrate the holiday was to offer a free meal to anyone who wanted one. He gathered volunteers and procured donated food from stores and farmers. The ladies of the church got out the white tablecloths and festive china and set the tables. The children in Sunday school made placemats, and everyone cooked. The first year we served thirty-five people, and six years later, 225. It was great. When I reminded him of all that, he just smiled, nodded.

"You're very quiet today," I said.

"I just want to look at you," he replied.

And for that I am extraordinarily thankful.

There is so much to be thankful for. I am thankful for Zoom. I am thankful for the caring staff who watch over Sky for me. I am thankful for the love and support of my family and friends. I am thankful for Tubby and Pogo, my feline housemates. I am thankful for all the natural world has to offer—sun and clouds, wind and rain, snow and trees, wild food and good soil to grow more. Chickadees and squirrels, geese and ducks, worms and ladybugs, spiders and frogs. Rocks and mountains, lakes and rivers, bogs and oceans.

Even though these strange times keep us from doing so many things we would love to do, we can be thankful for the simple pleasures—a hot cup of coffee or tea, the peacefulness of a snowfall, snuggles with a pet, a good book, a phone call with a friend.

Or take some advice from Tubby and Pogo—have a nap!

Hang in there, everyone.

JANE: A BITTERSWEET CHRISTMAS EVE

Thirty-five years ago today I packed up most of my belongings and put them in storage. Into my car went some clothes, a few favorite books, and my pillow, along with my four cats, Sage, Fern, Charlotte, and Violet (none of whom was too pleased). We headed north. Two hours later I arrived at my new home, Frog Run Farm, a commune in the Northeast Kingdom of Vermont, where Sky lived. (Sage howled the whole way.)

Sky met me in the dooryard. We took the cats to the dairy barn, their new home. We loaded my clothes, books, and pillow into two backpacks, put them on, and began the one-mile trek uphill into the woods to our new home. Over the previous two months, we had built a small, one-room cabin in those woods, with a sleeping loft, woodstove, and outhouse. It was my first adventure in house building. Before that, I was lucky to be able to figure out how to install a shelf.

It was the first day of my new life, living with Sky. We had only been together for ten months, but we both knew it was time to take the next step. With a light snow falling—as it is supposed to do in Vermont at Christmas—we settled in for the night. In bed, we held hands and sang Christmas carols, a tradition we would uphold for the next thirty-four years.

Thirty-four Christmas Eves and Christmas Days. First Dana came along, and then Sayer. We did all kinds of different things to celebrate the holiday—there are plenty of stories to tell. When Dana was almost two, we started the tradition of lighting one more candle every day until Christmas Eve. Dana loved the candles, but mostly she loved putting out the candles with the snuffer. That tradition has remained, no matter where Sky and I have been living during the month of December.

This year is different. Dana and I visited with Sky via Zoom this morning. He was pretty out of it, seemed sleepy, but with a staff member's urging, finally focused on the computer and our faces.

"You're alive!" he exclaimed. "You're alive!"

"Yup," Dana and I both answered. "Did you think we were dead?"

"Yes, yes! You were in a terrible accident—Sayer too. You were all dead. You're not dead?"

"No, we're fine. Sayer too. I guess this is the best Christmas present ever!"

Sky smiled.

"Well, at least he knows who we are," Dana and I agreed.

Tonight it is fifty degrees and raining. But no matter the weather, I light the twenty-four candles and pour myself a glass of wine. I may or may not be able to bring myself to sing any Christmas carols once I'm in bed. I am sad beyond belief, yet so grateful that Sky is getting excellent care—and that he knows that we are alive.

Merry Christmas to all who celebrate. And blessings on all of you in the new year. May I be able to touch Sky again. And then we will sing.

JANE: **THE LIGHT GROWS**

It is almost February 2, halfway between the winter solstice and the spring equinox. It was five below zero (Fahrenheit) this morning when I got up, and now it has warmed to a balmy six above. The sun is out, not a cloud in the sky, and no wind. I spent a little time outside, and with enough clothes on, it was actually pleasant. I watch the people ice fishing out on the lake—some have been out since dawn—and know that they are more rugged than I am. I like winter, but I am thrilled that the days are getting longer. The sun warms my house, and my spirit.

Sky (and most of the staff and residents of his facility) has received both doses of the vaccine. No side effects have been reported to me. That's good. But the "side effect" that I wait for is a change in the visiting policy. No word on that yet.

I continue Zoom visits with Sky, and the occasional phone call when he wants to talk with me. At the scheduled Zooms, I never know what will happen. One day he was "hiking" and had to get going, and the staff member graciously held the tablet next to Sky while he walked up and down the halls. Sky and I didn't speak much, but the staff member and I did, and I told him tales about Sky and his long-distance hiking experiences. Although I wasn't able to interact directly with Sky, I was pleased that the staff member now knew a little more about him, and who he had been, and that perhaps that would help in their day-to-day interactions.

Sky continues to fall periodically, and hurt himself in other ways. When he does that, the nurse is required to call and tell me. One time he hurt himself because he was on his hands and knees "fixing" the toilet. Another time he was on his hands and knees escaping a war. But whenever the nurse calls (with the calls always beginning, "It's not an emergency!"), she then goes on to tell me something Sky did or said recently that they found endearing.

"Your man is so funny! We just love him! One time, when it was National Grandparents' Day, he said, 'Been there, done that, it should be National Masturbation Day!' and we all burst out laughing." (OK, so Sky used to be a sex educator; this didn't surprise me.) Another time she said, "Sky just came around the corner and whispered to me, 'We should smoke some pot!'" (I could only roll my eyes and comment, "And he probably doesn't even know that it's not illegal anymore.")

I get reports of the calls he has with our daughter Dana, and his sister, Mary. They find the same things as I do— sometimes he's talkative, sometimes he's not; sometimes he can lift his head to look at the screen, sometimes he can't; sometimes he can answer questions, sometimes he can't; sometimes he can finish a thought, sometimes he can't.

But we all agree that we can still see Sky there—a tip of the head, a shrug of the shoulder, a chuckle, a song, a smile, a brief flitter of recognition when he can look at the screen. When he was first diagnosed, he was so worried about losing himself, but that hasn't happened. Sky is still there, it's just that sometimes he can't communicate that in words.

My garden seeds arrived a few days ago, and I've got a big bag of potting soil ready to go. It's too soon to plant the seeds, and I must be patient. But with the growing light, and the passage of time, I know the day will come when I can nestle those seeds in the soil. Then I will, once again, have to be patient as I wait for the plants to emerge. Those of you who know me well know that patience is not one of my virtues, so this is good practice for me.

Maybe with spring, and sprouting seeds, I will finally be able to visit Sky? In the meantime, I stay snug at home, grateful for the growing light.

. . . .

JANE: THE END IS A BEGINNING

And, just like that, it's over.

After being completely "normal," entertaining the staff and residents with his songs, humor, and antics, Sky was unable to bear weight on his left leg on Monday, February 15. X-rays showed no break in hip or pelvis. Doctor and staff were puzzled. He continued to not be able to bear weight, and cried out in pain whenever he was moved.

On Tuesday afternoon, I was granted permission for a "compassionate care visit"—my first time to be with Sky up close and personal for almost a year. On Wednesday morning, I arrived at his facility. I gowned, gloved, and masked, and was taken to his room where he sat uncomfortably in a wheelchair. I spent so much time hugging and kissing him, looking into his eyes. He was mostly unresponsive, but later "came to," called me by name, and said, "I know what I'm ready for."

"The next world?" I asked.

"Yes. I just want to rest." Then he went to bed for a nap, and he fell asleep while we held hands.

An enormous burden was lifted. I was allowed to visit him whenever I wanted.

I returned on Friday to watch his physical therapy appointment as the therapist worked his limbs and tested his strength to try and get him to stand—not to walk, but to be able to easily transfer from bed to chair and back again without using the Hoyer lift. He cried out "no!" and was in pain, and he physically tried to resist her moving certain body parts. Eyes closed, hands clenched. He was not a happy camper.

Later, when we were alone, he opened his eyes, looked at me, and smiled his sweet smile in recognition, then closed his eyes. My plan was to return on Monday for his next PT appointment.

Saturday evening I got a call from the nurse. He had aspirated some liquids and seemed to be losing his ability to swallow. Was it OK for him to have a puréed diet?

"How about no diet?" was my reply. Sky's greatest fear was that people would try to feed him when he did not want to be fed. I suggested stopping food altogether (they did). Then I asked, "Should I come in the morning?"

"Yes," was the reply.

So, Sunday morning, I packed a bag, left out enough food and water for my cats, and headed south to his facility. When would I be back home?

When I arrived, his breathing was very labored and I was sure he would die any minute. His out-of-state sisters all spoke their goodbyes to him with my phone held to his ear, and our kids—who live locally—arrived for their visits. Visiting was awkward, with gowns, masks, and gloves—damn this pandemic—so we didn't really have the family-hang-out time we would have had without COVID-19.

Sunday evening around six, he had about an hour of fairly lucid talking and singing—though we could only understand about a quarter of what he said, his voice was so soft, and Dana and I are not that great at Name that Tune.

At one point he said, "The end is near."

Dana asked, "How long?"

Sky replied, "Four or five," though when Dana pressed him, he could not say four or five what. We let it be. He closed his eyes, and drifted away. Dana went home, and the staff brought in a cot for me to spend the night.

Monday was a day of vigil, phone calls, texts, and emails to friends and family. I wanted to break the news that Sky was dying and not have people learn that he died out of nowhere. It was bittersweet. It was hard to explain to people that I was both very happy and very sad, all at the same time. Sky remained unresponsive, but not in pain, throughout the day and night.

Monday night into the wee hours of Tuesday (today) were a struggle for me while Sky "slept" along peacefully, thanks to the tender care of the staff. It was hard for me to sleep listening to his breaths, wondering if the next one would come or not. I managed only three hours, and finally got up and sat by his side until dawn.

I steeled myself for another long day of vigil as his condition, his breathing, had not changed in thirty-six hours. I was exhausted, and I wondered how long this could go on, how long I could go on.

The staff got me a delicious breakfast, and I was eating as the aides were bathing and changing him. He was on his side facing me, and it looked like he wasn't breathing, but then I saw a small breath. The women settled him onto his back, and then called to me.

He was not breathing, a blank look on his face. We all stared in shock, he took a tiny breath, and then was still.

My beloved and best friend is gone from this Earth. I will miss him dearly. But I am so glad this is over for him . . . and me.

Thank you all for following along on our journey. This blog meant the world to Sky.

ALZHEIMER'S CANYON
The End

[Our hero begins the ragged process of settling in to Alzheimer's Canyon, apparently his new residence.

Thanks to his invisible guide Dusty, he has a name now—X, short for X the Explorer. As well as a few basic supplies, like underwear, clothes, and food.

And he is finally rid of his unfortunate first fashion statement in Alzheimer's Canyon, the adult diapers supplied by the Shady Way Home.

As the darkness deepens, X notices new sounds drifting up from the valley. You might call it a howling, or maybe a groaning.]

"Dusty, what is that?"

"Ha! I think I might be right about you after all, my brother X. Y'all got some good instincts, boy! I didn't even have to knock you upside the head to be listening, and you *heard*."

"Yeah, but heard what, though? Is that a made-by-human noise or . . . or . . . what?"

"Let me guess, X. Ah reckon y'all never heard anything like that before."

"You're right there, Mr. Dusty. And I can't say as I mind missing out . . . whatever they doin' is some spooky shit!!"

"They just doin' their thing is all. Moanin', groanin', whatever. They be Sundowners doing their Sundowning thing. Won't never hurt nobody."

"Sundowners—that sounds like the band that played their three chords at my high school junior prom. These ones know a bit more about music, I'm guessing. Still, I'm glad they're down there and we're up here. Sundowners—that mean something, Mr. Dusty?"

"Wahl, it must to them, cuz they doing it whenever that sun goin' down, or up. Man, you got a whole lot to learn! You probably don't even see the lights, neither."

"Lights? Wait! What? Those white balloon thingies down there?"

"X, I'm trying to help y'all here, I really am. But *you* gotta hep yo' own side too. I will tell you again, but not many more times: Pay attention, now!! If you don't know what's goin' on, then you gotta pay *extra* attention, X. I don't want to lose y'all down here, little buddy."

And with that, Dusty pokes the fire one last time. Embers drift lazily. The Sundowners are calming themselves. A sparkling night settles over the seemingly endless Canyon.

"Dusty?"

"Yeah, bud."

"Thanks for keeping me alive."

"Sure, bud."

"Thanks to you, this'll be a day to remember always!"

"Good luck with that one, pal," Dusty murmurs.

EPILOGUE

It's been nearly a year since Sky died. I have passed through the seasons, tended my garden, relished in the harvest, and now, again, face the darkness of winter.

Time passes. Life goes on.

I'm sad every day that Sky is gone from this Earth. Often, it's simply hard to believe. While he was living at the memory care facility, I learned how to live without him, but I always knew he was still alive. Still living his life. Now I know he is gone, and I'm still learning how to live without him. And while I miss him terribly, I am also at peace knowing he is at peace.

I gave permission for an autopsy to be done. There is so much we don't know about dementia, and I was hoping it would help—someone, somewhere. It turns out that Sky's brain was riddled with both the plaques and tangles of Alzheimer's disease as well as Lewy bodies—the cause of his intense and nearly constant hallucinations. According to his doctor, it is very rare for there to be two kinds of dementia present to such an extent.

Now, as I reflect on our thirty-six years together, all we did and all we went through, I keep coming back to trust. We trusted each other deeply. That trust came in handy in all kinds of situations, from moving through changes in our relationship to raising our kids to living on a boat. But I realize now that Sky had to trust me completely while he was living with dementia. He had to trust that I wouldn't leave him, that I wouldn't lie to him, that I would keep him safe, that I wouldn't let him get lost. Our babies and children have to trust us, too, but that's all they've ever known. Sky, as a competent adult, never had to rely on anyone else to take care of his needs. As he gradually lost his skills, he had to trust me to take care of things. What a gift to be trusted like that.

I am grateful for honesty—Sky's especially. He wanted to talk about his dementia from the moment he received his diagnosis. He poured his heart out to me, to his sister, to one or two friends, to his children, to so many people he met on his journey, and in the blog. As he tried to find other people with dementia to talk with, he became so frustrated that most of them didn't want to talk about it, and that many denied that anything was even wrong. I cannot imagine what our time together would have been like if he had refused to acknowledge or talk about his life with dementia. Even though I often would resent him for waking me up to tell me something, I know now it was because he just had to share what was happening for him. Even though it eventually exhausted me, and led to him living in a memory care facility, I am grateful that he wanted to share his experience with me. When we were first together, we promised to always be honest with one another, to never lie. That created some challenging situations at times, but we knew we could work our way through it—because of honesty.

I never did learn patience. I would get mad at myself when I would snap at Sky, knowing that he couldn't help whatever he said or did. I had to let go of the Sky I had known and loved for so long as I watched him change. His essence was still the same—his "self"—but the intelligent, skilled, competent person I had fallen in love with gradually disappeared. He even lost patience with himself—a man who had always been incredibly patient, with me, with our kids, with his clients, with our various projects when they hit a snag. Now and then he even got mad and yelled out his frustration. In a way, I was glad I wasn't the only one who lost patience.

We learned to be flexible. We had already been pretty flexible as we raised children, cared for our homestead, built houses, lived on more than one boat, and dealt with the changes thrown at us from outside circumstances. But dementia caused us to become even more flexible. I felt like we were making things up as we went along, but it worked for us. There are so many books about caring for your loved one with dementia, but they really are no help. You've simply got to figure out your own situation as you go along. I'm glad we both had skills in that department, but they were certainly put to the test.

I'm starting to figure out what I'm going to do with my life now—remember "the end is a beginning"? I really don't want to be moving forward without Sky as my partner, but I am. There are many possibilities before me. I am not overwhelmed but am taking one step at a time. I am grateful for the love and care of my friends and family, for my grief support group, for my cats, and for the strength and solace of the natural world. Sky will always be with me. He was a gift. I hope you have found his words a gift too.

—Jane Dwinell, November 2021

JANE'S (AND SKY'S) HELPFUL HINTS

There are many books, websites, and classes to help people navigate having or caring for someone with dementia. Sky and I read many of them, perused an equal number of websites, and each took one (different) class. I didn't find any of it that helpful; what was helpful to me was the lived experience of others. That held true for Sky as well. He craved hearing the lived experiences of people with dementia—he was looking for a road map. But every dementia path is different, and there is no road map or visitor's guide. You may tire of hearing that, but it's absolutely true.

Here, in no particular order, are the things that Sky and I found useful on our journey:

Educate Yourself.

Read books, talk to people, take classes—do whatever appeals to you. Don't expect to be enlightened, but you will learn something, and you may meet people who will be helpful. Your Alzheimer's Association chapter may be helpful—or not. Your local memory clinic may be helpful—or not. Your local senior center may be helpful—or not. It's always worth trying. Check out your local memory care facilities, home care agencies, and adult day care centers so you know what is available should you need it. If you find yourself getting all wound up from too much information, then take a break. You don't need to know/do everything right now.

Take Care of the Legal Things.

Meet with an eldercare or estate attorney, and talk about your particular needs. Everyone should have a financial power of attorney, a health care power of attorney, an advance directive, and a will. These documents will bring peace of mind and make things easier on everyone. Depending on your financial situation, you may want to consider putting your assets into a trust. This will save the next of kin from having to go through probate court after the person with dementia (or anyone else in the family!) dies.

Start a Special Savings Account.

Depending on your financial situation, your assets, and/ or what kind of insurance or living situation you have, you may have to pay out of pocket for any care—everything from the hourly wages of in-home help to the daily rate of a memory care facility. None of it comes cheap. I am grateful I started putting money aside right away and had managed to collect enough that I wasn't (too) stressed by having to pay for Sky's care.

Find Support.

Whether it's professional support or friend-support, this is a tough and lonely journey full of surprises and twists and turns, and you'll need help—all of you. Don't be afraid to keep trying if you don't find something/someone that clicks right away. It was frustrating for us to try so many different support groups and therapists, but I eventually found my way to a group that was wonderful and exactly what I needed. Sky was not as fortunate, but I believe that he finally found what he was looking for in the memory care facility staff. You can turn to a social worker, therapist, clergy member, or an in-person or online support group. Or maybe your best friend will be enough.

Complete Your Bucket List.

Are there things you or your loved one have always dreamed of doing? Now is the time to do it! Don't wait—abilities can fall away pretty fast. I'm not just talking about strolling the streets of Paris or cruising the Caribbean, but doing things like sky diving, zip lining, river rafting, running a marathon, seeing a special play or concert, reading certain books, writing your memoirs, etc. Sky and I were blessed to have done so much traveling before his diagnosis, so his bucket list was pretty short. However, he didn't get to finish his memoirs—he started them too late. Don't make the same mistake!

Expect to Lose Friends and Family.

This is a tough and painful one. A dementia diagnosis is scary for everyone, and scary enough that a lot of people can't handle it . . . and they drift away. Unless they are someone incredibly special to you, just let them go. We found it wasn't worth our energy to try and chase those who couldn't bother to stick around. At the same time, nurture and show your gratitude for the friends and family who do stay by your side. They are priceless beyond measure.

Know Your Relationship will Change.

Whether the person with dementia is your spouse, parent, sibling, other relative, best friend, or colleague, your relationship will change. Don't expect things to stay the same. Spouses will no longer be equals. A child may have to parent the parent. A friend or sibling may have to take the lead. You may not be able to do the things you loved doing together previously—making music, hiking, playing games, sailing, biking, going out for a beer—and you'll need to find new ways to be together. It was awful to not be able to tell Sky everything anymore—it burdened him to hear my problems (whether or not they were related to his dementia). That's when trusted friends became so valuable to me, along with my journal.

Grieve the Changes.

Having dementia and being with someone with dementia is a series of losses, big and small. Know you will grieve each one. Don't try and shut your grief away—take time to talk about it, to cry, to write about it, to find a ritual of letting go. Anticipatory grief is tough . . . and never-ending. Celebrate the joys and honor the losses. For me, while I was incredibly sad when Sky died, I think my grief was less because I had spent so much time grieving already. Of course, our situation was complicated by the coronavirus pandemic (which brought on extra grief), so your journey may differ.

The Person with Dementia Is Always Right.

Even when they aren't. Don't try to argue with them or "set them straight." It's not going to work. If they think it's Monday when it's actually Tuesday, does it matter? If they think it's breakfast time instead of dinner time, does it matter? Just go along with them—you'll save yourself, and them, a lot of trouble. If you've always wanted to do improv theater, now's your chance! If the person is doing something dangerous, then it's important to redirect for their safety. You may have to be creative. Perhaps a hug, a dance, or a snack will be enough for them to move on to a different activity . . . or not. Expect the unexpected.

Keep Chaos to a Minimum.

We learned this one the hard way. Moving, house renovations, house building, and adopting new cats were not great activities for Sky. If you think you're going to need to do anything big, like move, do it as soon as possible. Once settled, stay settled. Don't rearrange the furniture or start in on new activities. Keep to the familiar—it will provide security for the person who is gradually losing their memory and their skills. If you have a schedule, stick to it. If you don't—Sky and I never did; we loved being spontaneous—you'll have to create one, and then stick to it. The goal is to create a safe space so the person with dementia can live their best life without fear.

Know Your Limits.

Caring for someone with dementia is incredibly hard work. I thought I'd be able to handle it easily since I had worked as a nurse in a memory care facility. Wrong. Professional staff work a shift and then go home; they're not with the person with dementia 24-7. They get a break. So make sure you get breaks! Whether that is taking short trips, bringing someone in for night duty, going out to lunch with a friend, or taking in a movie alone, do what you need to do to take care of yourself. And know that that may be the hardest thing you will have to do. You're no good to your loved one if your health and spirit start to fail. You're on call day and night and, at the same time, you're grieving the loss of so much. Give yourself a break. Forgive yourself for not being perfect. Ask for help. And if the day comes when you need to place your loved one in a memory care facility, do it. As horrible as it was to no longer be with Sky every day, it was absolutely the best thing for both of us.

ACKNOWLEDGMENTS

The road to this book has been long and hard. At times, I felt incredibly alone. At other times, thankfully, I felt great support. It's all part of the dementia journey.

So my deep gratitude goes to those of you who kept in touch with us on a regular basis by phone, email, and in-person visits. To those of you who went on bike rides and long walks with Sky, who took him out for breakfast and kept him for overnights, who had patience as his game- and card-playing skills slipped away. To those of you who shared bottles of wine with me over burgers and fries. To those of you who hosted me and Sky in your homes as we traveled around the country. To all the staff at the Arbors who cared for Sky with grace and love. While Sky was still alive, so much gratitude for my Caregivers' Support Group, a monthly Zoom meeting (before Zoom was popular!) of other retired colleagues who were also caring for loved ones; and now that he is gone, my monthly Grief Support Group, also made up of retired colleagues who have recently lost spouses.

I am not naming names, for fear of leaving someone out. But you know who you are!

Sky and I did many things together, but we always agreed that raising Dana and Sayer was the best thing we ever did with our lives. So here's to you, Dana, and your chosen family; and to Sayer and Emma for being such bright lights through this journey we did not ask to take. Your support and love is beyond compare.

But my deepest gratitude goes to Sky, who opened his heart to all of us. I am a better person for our thirty-six years together.

ABOUT THE AUTHORS

Sky Yardley and Jane Dwinell have been together since 1985. They raised two children, for many years had a small farm, and retired in their fifties to travel and do volunteer work. They both had successful careers—Sky as a family mediator, and Jane as an RN, freelance writer, and Unitarian Universalist minister. As an avocation, they designed and built seven houses and renovated two others. Sky was diagnosed with "probable early stage Alzheimer's disease" in the summer of 2016. He had been showing signs of memory loss since 2012, most significantly since 2015. He was 66 when he was diagnosed. Jane was 62. Sky died in 2021.

Also Available from Rootstock Publishing

All Men Glad and Wise: A Mystery by Laura C. Stevenson

The Atomic Bomb on My Back: A Life Story of Survival and Activism by Taniguchi Sumiteru

Blue Desert: A Novel by Celia Jeffries

Catalysts for Change: How Nonprofits and a Foundation are Helping Shape Vermont's Future by Doug Wilhelm

China in Another Time: A Personal Story by Claire Malcolm Lintilhac

Collecting Courage: Anti-Black Racism in the Charitable Sector edited by Nneka Allen, Camila Vital Nunes Pereira, & Nicole Salmon

An Everyday Cult by Gerette Buglion

Fly with a Murder of Crows: A Memoir by Tuvia Feldman

Hawai'i Calls: A Novel by Marjorie Nelson Matthews

Horodno Burning: A Novel by Michael Freed-Thall

The Hospice Singer: A Novel by Larry Duberstein

I Could Hardly Keep from Laughing: An Illustrated Collection of Vermont Humor by Don Hooper & Bill Mares

The Inland Sea: A Mystery by Sam Clark

Intent to Commit: A Novel by Bernie Lambek

A Judge's Odyssey: From Vermont to Russia, Kazakhstan, and Georgia, Then on to War Crimes and Organ Trafficking in Kosovo by Dean B. Pineles

Junkyard at No Town: A Novel by J.C. Myers

The Language of Liberty: A Citizen's Vocabulary by Edwin C. Hagenstein

A Lawyer's Life to Live: A Memoir by Kimberly B. Cheney

Lifting Stones: Poems by Doug Stanfield

CPSIA information can be obtained
at www.ICGtesting.com
Printed in the USA
BVHW041303021022
648427BV00001B/5